THE GARDEN
OF THE SPHINX

THE GARDEN OF THE SPHINX

150
Challenging and Instructive
Puzzles

Pierre Berloquin

TRANSLATED BY
Charles Scribner, Jr.

BARNES
&NOBLE
BOOKS
NEW YORK

1996 Barnes & Noble Books

ISBN 0-76070-116-4

Printed and bound in the United States of America.
M 9 8 7 6 5 4 3 2 1
FG

For Dominique
who so often knows why

CONTENTS

Solutions begin on page 83.

AUTHOR'S NOTE

These mathematical puzzles have appeared in the newspaper *Le Monde* during the past few years. A number of readers have responded to the challenge by offering not only original solutions and modes of attack but also by stating new problems related to those proposed. A dialogue was thus initiated in which my problems or those I reproduced from the literature generated a new set by stimulating the minds of my correspondents. This book presents a collection resulting from the fruitful exchange.

PREFACE

If one is being beaten over the head, it is a delight when the blows come to an end, and so it is with brain teasers when they solve themselves. I said: *when* they do.

But there is also a kind of gentle creaking sound in the act of thought when the clue eludes us and a pleasing sort of fury when the last hope turns out wrong, after which the mind goes into a panic as it turns and turns in a vicious cycle.

Yet anxiety can prove delightful, too, while one catches on to the threat of a paradox, even though contradictory results in computation darken one's understanding. Puzzles, paradoxes, and mental mazes form a grand trinity presiding over the play of mind, and I have long partaken of the bitter brew supplied by enigmas and conundrums.

All these mysteries have opened my eyes to the nature of the world of play. I have learned to suspect the trap concealed under some innocent statement and the dead end around the corner from common sense. Never again shall I take the world for a simple business. I have left the common ground for the Garden of the Sphinx where, remote from the deceitful platitudes of everyday life, I shall forever be found seeking *the solution*.

PROBLEMS

1. Water in the Desert

The desert lies before you. Your mission is to plant a flag a four days' march into the interior. You do not have any special equipment and must rely on your own powers, although you may enlist the help of one or more companions.

Carrying food and the flag itself is not a problem. The only limitation has to do with water: each person can carry only a five-day supply of water. Thus, if you went by yourself, the amount of water you could bring with you would take you only two and a half days toward your destination and back to your starting point. Given these conditions, how can you fulfill your mission without using more than a twenty-day supply of water and without enlisting more than three companions?

2. Pure Reason

At the beginning of this century, long before groups and relations were in vogue, algebra itself was not well received in educational circles. There was some doubt as to its pedagogical value. Logical arguments were considered preferable to unknowns and equations. Here we have an opportunity to return to that era and rediscover the utility of "pure reason."

It takes a train 7 seconds to pass by a stationary observer and 26 seconds to traverse the length of a station 380 meters long.

What is the speed of the train and its length?

3. The Age of His Digits

Let us remain pure. Here again, as in the case of the enigma in problem 2, unknowns and equations are not permitted. How old was a person in 1898 if the age in question is the sum of the digits of the year of his birth?

4. The Exchange of Knights

This problem can be solved directly by prolonged trial and error, but it is more interesting to solve it more systematically by means of a shortcut.

On a chessboard of three files and four ranks, three black nights (black stars) are face-to-face with three white knights (white stars). How many moves does it take for the black knights to change places with the white ones?

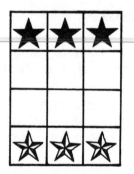

5. Squaring the Maltese Cross

In spite of the fact that the shape of the Maltese cross is radically different from that of the Greek cross, it is possible to transform it into a Greek cross. Several cuts with a pair of scissors and reassembling of the pieces correctly are all it takes. Can you find the solution with eight pieces?

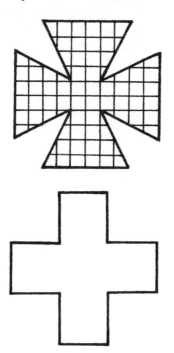

6. Reconstructing Octagons

A decoupage problem consists of cutting up one figure in order to reassemble its pieces in the shape of another figure. A closely related problem is one of assembling—starting with several figures of identical shape and then cutting them into pieces as economically as possible in order to reconstruct a similar figure of greater size.

Are you able to cut these three little octagons into a total of ten pieces and then reconstruct a single octagon with three times the area?

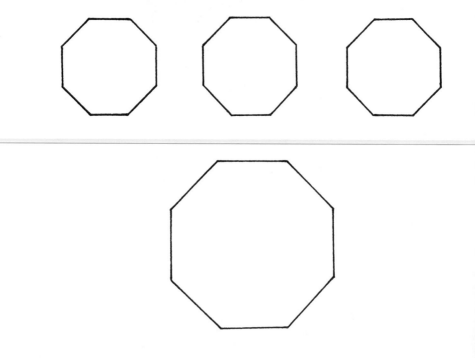

7. Basic Multiplication

There is a crude way of performing multiplications that requires nothing more than the ability to double and to halve (i.e., to multiply and to divide by 2). For instance, suppose we want to multiply 43 by 81. The two numbers are written at the top of two columns. In one column, a number is successively divided by two, disregarding remainders. In the other column the second number is successively multiplied by two until both columns have the same number of lines. The numbers on the right corresponding to any even numbers on the left are bracketed. The remaining ones are added up to give the correct product. Can you explain why?

43	81
21	162
10	324 ( )
5	648
2	1 296 ( )
1	2 592
	3 483

8. A World of Fours

The expressions that employ as digits only three 4s and the conventional mathematical symbols are endlessly varied.

$$\frac{4 \times 4!}{4}$$

$$4 \times 4^4$$

$$4 \times 4 \times 4!!$$

A little research shows that one can represent most values of the positive integers, assuming a resourceful use of arithmetic operations.

But is it possible to construct a universal formula adaptable to the expression of any positive integer n?

If necessary, one can use an unlimited number of operations.

9. Circular Uncertainties

A chord is drawn in a circle in a random way. What is the probability that its length is greater than the side of an inscribed equilateral triangle?

One way to calculate that would be to choose, for reasons of symmetry, the direction of the chord and to consider its intersection with the perpendicular diameter. The chord is of maximum length when it intersects the diameter in the middle of the radius. The probability in question is therefore ½.

Another method would be to consider the midpoint of the chord. This midpoint must lie within a concentric circle of half the radius. Since the area of the new circle is one quarter as large, the probability in question is ¼.

Joseph Bertrand proposed this problem half a century ago as a means of criticizing continuous probabilities and added a third method of calculation that leads to a result contradicting the two preceding results.

What is this method?

10. The Random Chord

If a chord is drawn on a circle "at random," the probability that it will be greater than the side of an inscribed equilateral triangle depends on the point of view of the calculator (see problem 9) and may be ½, ⅓, or ¼.

A reader of *Le Monde* has shown that if one adheres to the ambiguous reasoning that has produced the paradox, one can contrive to "vary" the probability in a continuous fashion between 0 and 1. By what construction can that variable probability be produced?

11. What Coincidences?

Is it possible that one could suddenly wake up, look at the alarm clock, and say, "That's strange! It has only one hand." At that instant, the three hands of the clock coincided exactly.

The three hands of the clock, which indicate the hour, the minute, and the second, are in exact alignment at twelve o'clock. Can they coincide at any other time in twelve hours?

12. Meetings on the Dot

The hour, minute, and second hands of an ordinary alarm clock cannot coincide exactly (except at twelve.o'clock). At what other moment in the day are the three hands closest to perfect alignment, or, in other words, lying within the smallest acute angle?

13. Steer Metabolism

A diet with precise goals is not always as simple as it seems. Have you any idea what it entails? A steer weighing 630 kilograms requires 13,500 calories a day for its "maintenance fodder," which keeps it as it is, in good health and without getting fatter. That amount of food turns out to be proportional to its external surface. How many calories does a steer of 420 kilograms require for its maintenance fodder?

14. Lightning Calculators

"Bona fide" calculating prodigies in reality combine exceptional abilities with certain simple calculations in order to conserve their energies. Suppose that one of these should undertake to calculate in his head the sixty-fourth root of a twenty-digit number. If he knows in advance that the result is an integer, does he need to know all the digits of the first number?

15. Heterogeneous Squares

Classically, a square containing the first of n^2 integers is "magic" when its lines, columns, and diagonals all add up to the same sum. Can one imagine a property opposite to magic? Is there such a thing as nonmagic? A first step consists of defining "heterogeneous squares." In such a square, each of the sums of its lines, columns, and diagonals would be different. Why is there no heterogeneous square of order 2 (containing 1, 2, 3, 4)? Can you construct one for order 3?

16. Antimagic

In an "antimagic" square the negation is more systematic than in a heterogeneous square (see problem 15). The sums of the rows, columns, and diagonals are not just different: they must form a sequence. There is no antimagic square of order 3, and the existence of one appears to be impossible. Can you construct one of order 4 (there are twenty known examples) and one of order 5?

17. Strategic Dates

Two contestants play at exchanging dates. (They do not take the year into account.) The first must name a day in January, for example, January 14. Then each player in turn picks a later day, retaining either the month or the date just named by his adversary.

For example, after January 14, it is possible to name January 16 or January 20, April 14 or October 14. One contest might begin as follows: January 14, April 14, April 27, April 30, June 30 . . .

The winner is the first to reply December 31. Which of the players is able to clinch the victory by an unbeatable strategy and how?

18. Manual Tactics

Two players compete with one another by exchanging prime numbers by signs. Each player, in turn, holds up a number of fingers on one hand. (Zero is not allowed.) The cumulative total must remain a prime number. One match might run as follows:

    A: 1
    B: 1 (+ 1 = 2)
    A: 3 (+ 2 = 5)
    B: 2 (+ 5 = 7)

What unbeatable strategy can the first player adopt?

19. Two-Handed Confrontations

Two contestants compete by exchanging prime numbers by digital signs as in problem 18. But this time each player in turn can use the fingers of one or both hands, zero again being excluded.

What is the winning strategy available to the one who plays first?

20. The Best Bridge

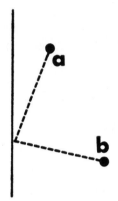

Two towns are situated on the same shore of a river. The bank of the river forms a straight line. There is a project to build a road that extends in a straight line from one town to a bridge across the river and then extends in a straight line to the second town. In this way the same bridge can serve both towns as a means of crossing the river.

What is the simplest way to find the best place to build the bridge, the goal being to minimize the length of the road from one town to the other?

21. The Best Place for the Bridge

The towns a and b are situated on opposite sides of a canal, the banks of which form two parallel lines. In this case, as distinguished from problem 20, the width of the canal must be taken into account. The object is to plot a road in a straight line from town a to a point c' on the canal, where there is a bridge perpendicular to the banks of the canal, across the bridge to the point d on the other side and then proceed in a straight line to town b. Where should the bridge $c'd$ lie to provide the shortest path from town a to town b?

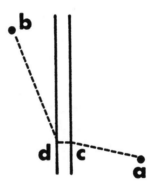

22. Thrift in Mirrors

It would seem that we live in an excessively luxurious world. Even our mirrors are larger than they need to be. If I am five feet six inches tall, how high a vertical mirror do I need to see all of me at once if I stand in front of it and do not move my head?

23. Multiple Images

I am at a point in front of two mirrors that rotate about a vertical axis lying in the plane that bisects them.

Depending on the angle between the mirrors, how many images of myself will I see?

24. A False Proof

Yes, your memory serves you well. There is only one perpendicular from a point to a plane. In that case, what is wrong with the following demonstration, which "proves" that there is an infinity of perpendiculars from an external point to a given plane? Let p be the external point and a and b be two arbitrary points on the plane. Two spheres with diameters pa and pb cut the plane in two circles that intersect at c and d. Since c is on the circles of diameters pa and pb (the great circles of the spheres), pc is orthogonal to ca and cb, and therefore to the plane. Likewise, d is certainly on the circles of diameters pa and pb, and po is orthogonal to da and dp, and accordingly, orthogonal to the plane. Whatever the points a and b may be, c and d can have an infinite number of values, and thus there are an infinite number of perpendiculars.

25. Visualizing Tetrahedrons

How good is your geometric imagination? Are you able to visualize in three-dimensional space? Are you able to construct eight tetrahedrons (not necessarily regular), in pairs, each having a portion of a side in common? This common portion may not be reduced to a line or point, nor can it be shared by more than two of the tetrahedrons.

26. Truth and Brotherhood

There are two brothers who are both scrupulously truthful, with only one exception: each one lies about his birthday on the day of his birthday.

If you ask them on New Year's Eve what their birthdays are, one will say "yesterday" and the other will say "tomorrow." On New Year's Day, they both give the same answers. What is the birthday of each?

27. Doubts About Euclid

Is the parallel axiom really necessary? Here is a proof that does not employ it in order to establish a theorem that could be substituted for the famous axiom.

Let us "show" that if two parallel lines are cut by a transversal, the sum of the interior angles on the same side of the transversal is equal to two right angles. Let a, b, c, and d be the internal angles determined by the transversal. Three hypotheses are possible, depending on whether the sum of the angles on the same side are (1) greater than two right angles; (2) less than two right angles; (3) equal to two right angles.

The first hypothesis entails that $a + d > 180°$, $b + c > 180°$, and therefore $a + b + c + d > 360°$. But $a + b = c + d = 180°$, from which it follows that $a + b + c + d = 360°$.

The hypothesis is contradictory and must be abandoned; the same thing occurs with the second by reversing the inequalities. There is only one remaining possibility: the sum of the internal angles is equal to two right angles.

Where is the error in this line of reasoning?

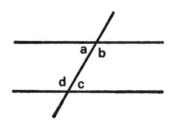

28. The Sum of the Angles

As a further doubt about the validity of the parallel postulate (see problem 27), one can appear to prove directly that the sum of the angles of any triangle is equal to 180°.

Take any triangle and divide it arbitrarily into two triangles. The internal angles of the figure are a, b, c, d, e, and f. Let us designate as x the sum of the angles of a triangle—what we are seeking to determine.

We have $a + b + f = x = c + d + e$ and $a + b + c + d + e + f = 2x$. But e and f, being adjacent and supplementary, have the sum 180°. Therefore:

$$a + b + c + d + 180° = 2x$$
$$x + 180° = 2x$$
$$x = 180°$$

Where is the error?

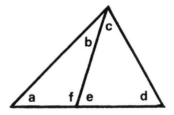

29. Jet Psychology

A cylindrical container 4 meters high is full of water. Three holes are made in it in a vertical row, 1, 2, and 3 meters from the ground, respectively. How will the drops of water land that spurt from the container at the beginning of the experiment? Will they strike the ground at the same place, and, if not, how will their points of fall be distributed in relation to the container?

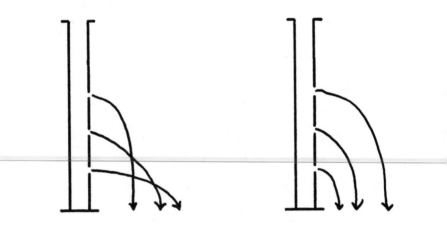

30. The Parson and His Sexton

A parson once said to his sexton, "Today I saw three of our parishioners. The product of their ages was 2,450. Can you tell me what their ages were?"

Sexton: No.

Parson: If I add that the sum of their ages is twice yours, can you give me the answer?

Sexton: Not yet.

Parson: I'll also tell you that the oldest is older than I am.

Sexton: Now I have all the information I need.

If we assume that the parson and his sexton are both able mathematicians, what are the ages of the three parishioners?

31. Revealing Ambiguities

Simon and Paul are two friends; x and y are two integers between 2 and 99, inclusive. The only thing that Simon knows about the two integers is their sum, $x + y$, while the only thing Paul knows about them is their product, xy. In this situation, each of them attempts to identify x and y.

Simon says to Paul: "I do not have enough information."

Paul replies: "Me, neither."

At that point Simon says, "Now I do."

Then Paul says, "So do I."

Can you determine a pair of numbers consistent with their dialogue?

32. An Illegitimate Equilateral Triangle

Inasmuch as it is impossible to trisect an angle using only a compass and straightedge, classical geometry takes very little interest in the triangle formed by the trisectors of an arbitrary triangle. It is, in fact equilateral, as is usually established by trigonometry. Nevertheless, it is possible to prove it geometrically. Can you demonstrate such a theorem?

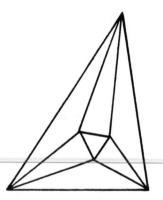

33. Division by Geometry

Is 54 divisible by 3? In geometry that is not always evident. Let us test it by experiment.

In this rectangle of 56 squares, two squares have been removed, leaving 54—a number divisible by 3. Is it possible to cover all the squares of the remaining figure with triple dominoes (i.e. units made up of three squares in a row)?

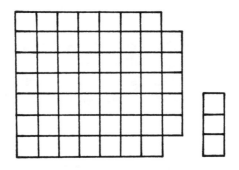

34. Dismembering One Thousand

The number 1,000 can be expressed in a great many ways as the sum of four even positive integers (zero excluded). For example, 1,000 = 2 + 4 + 66 + 928. It can also be expressed in a great many ways as the sum of four odd integers, such as 1 + 3 + 5 + 991 = 1,000. Of these two ways of breaking up 1,000, which are the more numerous, the sums of even numbers or of odd numbers?

35. How Many Elevators?

An apartment house has seven floors (above the ground floor) and a number of elevators. Each elevator travels between the ground floor and the seventh floor. But in order to conserve energy, each elevator stops only at three of the six intermediate floors. Its stops at the other three are omitted. Since it is desirable to be able to get from any floor to any other floor without having to change elevators, how many elevators must be installed, and what floors do they serve?

36. The Queen Takes a Walk

The queen in chess is able to cover every square in the standard 8 × 8 chessboard and return to her starting point in sixteen moves. This kind of closed circuit ends up at the starting point, but if one permits her to traverse a single square several times, she can accomplish her trip in only fourteen moves. How can one plot that trip (which is the shortest one achieved to date)?

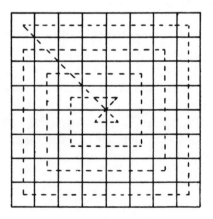

37. An Attractive Number

The number 495 has a strange attraction for three-digit numbers. For example, take any three-digit number (in which the digits are not all the same); for this case, let us pick 265. Rearrange its digits in decreasing order to produce 652. Now reverse the order of the digits to 256 and subtract the last number from the next-to-last one: 652 − 256 = 396. Perform the same operation on 396: 963 − 369 = 594. Do the same for 594: 954 − 459 = 495. As Kaprekar discovered, no matter what number you start with, it will invariably lead to 495. Why is that?

38. If and Only If

A businessman wishes to give salary increases to two of his three employees: Tom, Dick, and Harry. He has arrived at a statement that summarizes the logical problem presented by the choice he must make. If and only if I give Tom or Dick or both a raise and do not raise Harry, then I shall raise Tom; and if I raise Dick, I shall raise Harry.

In light of this condition, who will get a raise?

39. Curvilinear Mystery

Curvilinear figures are more mysterious than rectilinear ones. Can you calculate the area of the curvilinear square produced by the four quarter circles centered on the apexes of the big square?

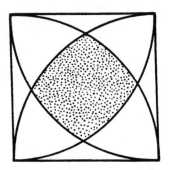

40. Less Water in the Desert

Nothing is more stimulating to the intellect than a desert trip. Following the publication of problem 1 and its solution, I received numerous letters from readers who succeeded in planting the flag in the required spot and at the same time using less than fifteen days' worth of water and also with a reduced crew. Can you figure out how that can be done?

41. Superfluous Digits

This example of long division is uniquely determined by the single digit appearing in the quotient. All the missing digits, which are indicated by dots, can be deduced. See if you can recover them.

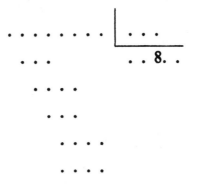

42. A Difficult Juncture

What happens when two cylinders intersect? Take two cylinders of radius 1 whose axes of symmetry are perpendicular to one another in the same plane. What is the volume of their intersection?

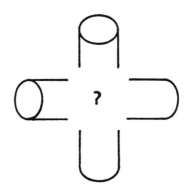

43. Using Your Imagination

You are given a three-digit number, the last, middle, and first digits of which are the 100th, 200th, and 300th digits, respectively, in the decimal expansion of π. Square the number, double the result, and raise the double of the square to the fifth power. Now subtract the next-to-last result from the last. Without using mathematical tables, calculators, or extensive computation, can you determine the units digit of the number resulting from the final subtraction?

44. Father, Son, and Horse

A man and his son must make a 60-kilometer journey. They have a horse for the trip that is able to average 12 kilometers an hour. The problem is that the horse can carry only one person at a time. If one person rides, the other must walk. Assuming that the father walks at a rate of 6 kilometers an hour and his son 8, how many hours will the trip take if they arrive at their destination at the same time?

45. Archimedes Trisects the Triangle

One of the most famous insoluble problems of geometry is to find a general method of trisecting an angle by means of a straightedge and compass only. In this case, "insoluble" does not mean that the correct construction has eluded mathematicians up to now; rather, that it has been demonstrated to be impossible in *principle*, since the problem is equivalent to finding a general solution to the equation of the third degree without any irrational number other than $\sqrt{2}$.

On the other hand, if one liberalizes the "rules" of the problem to permit devices in addition to the straightedge and the compass, it can be readily solved. One method, attributed to Archimedes, depends on inscribing on a separate piece of paper (or on the straightedge itself) marks representing the distance between the endpoints of a line segment. Can you reconstruct that method?

46. Predictable Pain

A logician once observed that one of his eyelashes was growing into his eye and was irritating the cornea. So he plucked it out. When the complaint recurred, he decided to study the problem. In this way, he noticed that the irritation flared up two days later, and two days after that, and then at successive intervals of 5, 3, 1, 3, 4, 3, 3, 2, 2, 6, 1, 2, etc. Has our logician grounds for continuing to believe that the eyelash follows a regular and predictable growth pattern? Is he able to deduce a precise law governing the phenomenon?

47. Watch Out for the Train

A man is walking along a one-way railway bridge. He is two-thirds of the way over it when he sees a train approaching him at the rate of 45 miles per hour. In this situation he is able to escape in the nick of time by running at a constant speed. The interesting thing is that it makes no difference in which direction he runs. Without any algebra or any equation, can you calculate his speed?

48. Knight Moves

On this chessboard of 3 × 3 squares, a knight can make sixteen different moves (two moves from each of the outer squares).

How many moves can it make from a chessboard 7 × 9, or more generally, $p \times q$?

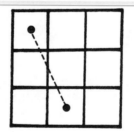

49. Playing with Blocks

A set of children's blocks has exactly the right number of pieces to construct two separate squares or a cube, the side of which is equal to the difference between the sides of the two squares. What is the smallest number of blocks for such a set, and what are the two constructions?

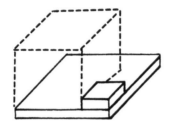

50. IQ Logic

In this puzzle, let us grapple with the sort of problem in arithmetic reasoning that has become such a fixture in intelligence tests. We start with the sequence

$$\frac{1}{5} \quad \frac{1}{45} \quad \frac{1}{117} \quad \frac{1}{221} \quad \frac{1}{357} \cdots$$

If the terms of this sequence follow a logical pattern, what is the next fraction? What is the sum of the first thirteen terms?

51. Magic Cubes

Filling in a magic square takes care and time. You have to distribute the first n^2 whole numbers in conformity with $2n + 2$ constraints: the sums of the lines, columns, and diagonals have to be equal to one another. But to fill in a magic cube calls for the next higher degree of patience, for you must distribute n^3 whole numbers in conformity with $6n + 4$ constraints: to create this equality along the edges and the four long diagonals. Can you fill a $3 \times 3 \times 3$ cube with the first 27 whole numbers?

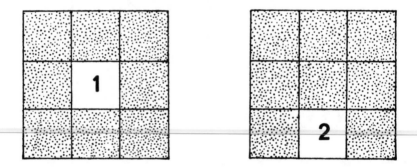

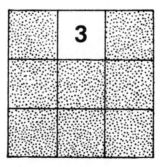

52. Three Strokes of the Compass

The construction of the mean proportional is one of the most standard of all geometric operations, provided one assumes the right to draw parallel lines. But do you know the simplest way of performing the construction? If lengths *a* and *b* are lying suitably on a straight line, their mean proportional can be determined by three applications of a compass. How?

53. To Be Continued

1, 2, 3, 4, 5 . . .

What is the next number? Facing such a question on an intelligence test is enough to daunt the most inventive minds, which are often able to come up with a number of answers, in addition to 6. A handbook of integral sequences contains no fewer than twenty-two integral sequences, all starting with 1, 2, 3, 4, 5. Some of them go beyond 10 in their similarity to the sequence of natural numbers. Can you find at least six such sequences?

54. Five Folds

Given a piece of paper in the shape of a square, without using any instrument, how can one produce a smaller square the area of which is three-quarters that of the original square?

55. Nine Lines Make Twenty-One Triangles

Arranged symmetrically in this particular way, nine lines produce only nine triangles, provided one does not count the triangles that overlap one another. But it is possible to improve this score considerably. In fact, it is possible that nine lines can produce at least twenty-one non-overlapping triangles.

56. A Cube of Bricks

We have on hand twenty-seven parallelepiped bricks measuring $2 \times 1 \times \frac{1}{2}$. How can one assemble these to produce a cube of dimensions $3 \times 3 \times 3$?

57. Kicking a Goal

A soccer player in possession of the ball is running down a sideline toward the opposing goalposts. Along that line, what is the best point for him to shoot a goal? In other words, what is the point when the goalposts can be seen to offer the widest angle? One supposes that the field is 100 meters long and 70 meters wide. The goalposts are 7.32 meters apart.

58. Other People's Husbands

In a situation that has become a classic one in puzzle literature, n married couples find themselves on the bank of a river they wish to cross. They have at their disposal a boat that can hold only $(n - 1)$ persons at one time. The logic of the situation demands that no wife be on the bank or in the boat without her husband if other husbands are there, even if the other husbands are accompanied by their wives. Supposing that n is equal to or greater than 7, how many crossings are necessary?

59. Sequences and Gaps

There are a great many plausible sequences of integers starting 1, 2, 3, 4, 5 that are otherwise different. This was shown to be so in problem 53. But it is possible to go further in that direction. In fact, it is possible to find an infinite number of sequences that begin with 1, 2, 3, 4, 5 and continue beyond 10, 100, or any number you may choose. Yet each one of these will contain a gap somewhere beyond the last number specified, no matter how large that number may be. How can a simple formula define such a sequence? Obviously, a formula like "all the whole numbers except 53" is unacceptable. For example, what sequence starts with 1, 2, 3, 4, 5, 6, 7, 8, 9, 10, 11, 12 and does not contain 13?

60. Trick Squares

Given a checkerboard, for example, one with sixteen squares (4 × 4), how does one fill the squares with numbers in compliance with the following three rules:

1) Each square contains a positive integer greater than 1.
2) The integers in two squares meeting along a line have a common factor.
3) The integers in two squares meeting at a single point have no common factor.

It is possible to fill this kind of square, which we shall call a "trick square" (since the name "magic" is used elsewhere). The problem is What are the smallest numbers that will work?

61. Circles and Square Roots of Seven

In geometry at least, the circle is all-important and deserves admiration, if not veneration. For geometers obsessed with the beauty of the circle, Quimper de Lanascol even invented a word, "cyclolatry," in his voluminous work on the geometry of the compass in which he compiled the constructions possible with the use of a compass alone. One of these beautiful constructions is that of the length of the square root of seven, given a unit length. Do you know how to represent that with only four arcs of a circle and without a straightedge?

62. An Adequate Supply of Digits

In connection with this puzzle, let us deal with the concerns of the now virtually obsolete profession of compositors.

It requires eleven digits to print all the numbers from 1 to 10 and one hundred ninety-two digits to print all the numbers from 1 to 100.

Now let us approach the question in a more general way. How many digits does one need to print all the numbers from 1 to N if N has m digits?

63. Pawn Parity

On a checkerboard of n dimensions on which the lower left-hand square is black (as on a regular chessboard), one places pawns in such a way that there is exactly one pawn assigned to any row and column.

Is the number of pawns on the white squares always odd or even, or can it vary?

64. Trick and Countertrick

On the basis of trick squares (see problem 16), a puzzle fan has proposed the construction of antitrick squares in which the basic relations have been inverted to require a common factor at each angle and relatively prime numbers for adjacent columns.

His smallest solution is:

115	52	33	56
26	15	28	99
51	14	45	76
112	156	38	135

Is there a smaller one with its highest number less than 156?

65. Squaring a Star

Is it possible to cut this star into eight pieces that can be reassembled into a square? What is the most symmetrical solution?

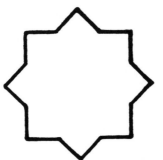

66. Matchmaking

The art of linking matches provides interesting analytical problems that require care and thought. For a given number of matches, one must find the two-dimensional diagrams in which each match touches at least one other at an endpoint. Thus, there are only three ways of connecting three matches and five ways of connecting four. In how many ways can one connect five matches or six or seven or eight . . . ?

67. Prime Magic

8	1	6
3	5	7
4	9	2

This magic square is the smallest one formed by nine consecutive integers. For its size, it is unique and nearly symmetrical in all its internal relations. Its columns, rows, and diagonals all have the same sum: 15. If we should decide to make such a square using prime numbers only, what is the smallest possible square?

68. Constructive Folds

A piece of paper not only gives a mathematician something to write on; it also gives a tool for the study of plane geometry. Its folds are automatically rectilinear and determine straight lines. Various folds also provide certain relations, certain bisectors, etc. By folding a square piece of paper, is it possible to construct a regular hexagon?

69. Three and Five Make Four

A well-known problem consists in taking an 8-pint container filled with water, plus two empty containers of 5 and 3 pints, and then using these to measure out exactly 4 pints in the simplest way.

Can you avoid trial and error and come up with a systematic and elegant solution to this problem?

70. The Price Is Right

Every morning a radio station gives its listeners the chance to win an expensive prize, which is described in detail except for its brand. Ten listeners attempt successively to name the exact retail price (a whole number of dollars). For each of their guesses the MC indicates whether it is correct, too high, or too low. The first listener to give the right price wins the prize. There is a strategy that will ensure a win if one person were able to make all ten guesses or if ten listeners were able to follow a single strategy by teaming up. Can you describe such a strategy?

71. Newton's Steers

Tradition attributes to Newton a curious problem that can be solved without using calculus.

In twelve days, seventy-five steers crop a 60-acre field, while eighty-one steers crop a 72-acre field in fifteen days. How many steers would it take to crop a 96-acre field in eighteen days? (It is stipulated that the grass grows uniformly in all the fields and is the same height in all of them at the beginning of the problem.)

72. Sixteen Equals Four Times Fifteen

Following up on several problems of aligning points, a puzzle fan came up with a way of distributing sixteen points on a plane that will simultaneously create fifteen alignments of four points. Here is one of the solutions:

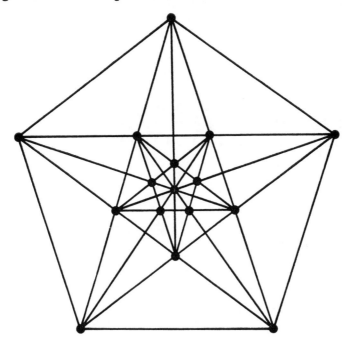

Can you find another?

73. Truncated Cubes

Are you as well acquainted as you should be with the properties of polyhedrons—those special shapes that play such important roles in the organization of space itself?

The cube, in spite of its apparent simplicity, is a polyhedron rich in various symmetries. It holds in addition to its planes of symmetry six axes of order 2, four axes of order 3, and three axes of order 4. We shall not provide a diagram here. It is a tricky task to visualize the transformations of these axes as the result of various truncations of the cube. What will they become if one lops off

1) an apex in order to create an equilateral triangle?
2) two apexes diametrically opposed in the same way?
3) four apexes that are not adjacent?

74. Leaping Counters

Twelve numbered positions are arranged in a circle. One starts four counters marked *a*, *b*, *c*, *d* placed on the numbers 1, 2, 3, 4. A counter moves from one position to another by jumping four places (empty or filled) in clockwise or counterclockwise direction in order to land in a fifth position, which must be empty. After a certain number of such displacements, the four counters will end up in the original four places, the order of the counters being either the original one or a new one.

In how many different sequences can the four counters end up in the first four positions?

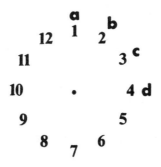

75. Trickery and Magic

Does magic adapt itself to trickery as it permits "antitrickery" as defined in problem 60? There exists at least one square 4 × 4 filled with whole numbers such that all the rows, columns, and the two diagonals add up to the same sum. The numbers that are in vertical or horizontal contact with one another are relatively prime. Those that are at an angle to one another have at least one common divisor. This is what we have decided to call a supertrick square. Can you construct it?

76. Black and White Dots

Here is one of the ways of arranging ten dots in five alignments of two black dots and two white dots. How would you arrange twenty-one dots in fourteen alignments of two black dots and two white dots each?

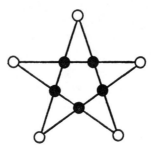

77. Christmas Dinner

For six brothers of a certain family, Christmas and New Year's Day are the two traditional occasions to dine together with their six wives. The meals take place at a single round table where the brothers sit according to their ages, always in the same chairs. They leave between them empty places for their wives, none of whom sits beside her husband.

If the wives never sit in the same positions twice, how many years will it take for them to exhaust all the possible seating arrangements?

78. Flawless Cubes

Constructing cubes constitutes an unlimited universe of puzzles, some of which are as difficult as anyone could ask for. In a "simple" puzzle, one is set the problem of constructing all the 3 × 3 × 3 cubes that can be made out of L-shaped tricubes (i.e., a solid figure in which three cubes are joined at right angles). The diagram below shows one solution. In the lower left-hand corner of each layer, a dot indicates that the tricube extends upward from the page. But this assemblage has a "flaw" inasmuch as certain pairs of tricubes overlap each other in such a way that both are in the same vertical or horizontal layer. Is it possible to overcome this defect?

79. What Times Are They?

With two ears, how many chiming clocks can you follow at one time?

There are two such clocks that are out of synchrony by three seconds at most. They happen to chime the same time at a certain hour. The strokes of the one occur every five seconds. The other's strokes are every four seconds. Your ears will confuse two strokes if there is a smaller interval than a second between them. If one hears a total of thirteen strokes, what time is it?

80. Beyond Thirst

Let us make a determined—though purely theoretical—assault on the problem of thirst. It is obligatory to plant a flag in the desert a four-day march from the starting point. The number of companions can be as many as one chooses, but none of them can bring more than a five-day supply of water. We have already had a solution involving a twenty-day supply of water (problem 1) and a fourteen-day supply (problem 40). Can you cut this supply further by a few days' worth? To do this, you may have to overcome a slight inhibition.

81. Kings, Queens, and Knaves

Three players divide up a pack of fifty-two playing cards in a random way into three "hands," not all with equal numbers of cards. Then each player takes one of these hands, the third player having the smallest. In looking at their cards, each of the first two players notices that if he should draw at random two cards from his hand, there is only one chance in two that neither of them will be a face card (i.e., a jack, queen, or king).

How many face cards are there in the third hand?

82. Folding, Folding

The folding of paper offers numerous resources for geometric constructions, even though it's possible only to determine the bisector of an angle or the middle of a line and the perpendicular to it (see problem 68).

The figure below shows one way of making an octagon appear on a square sheet of paper. The paper is folded into four squares. Each square is folded into two isosceles triangles. The bisectors of the two demi–right angles give the sides of an octagon. The sides are clearly equal, and one can verify that all the angles equal 135°.

Can you find another, completely different method of determining an octagon by folding a square sheet of paper?

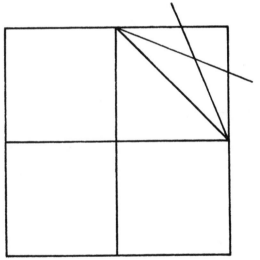

83. Whodunit?

Three suspects testify as follows:
    A: B is guilty.
    B: A just lied.
    C: A is guilty.
    A: The next statement of C will be true.
    B: The last statement of A is false.
    C: The two last statements of A are false.
Who is guilty?

84. A False Unknown

A	B	C	X
D	E	C	D
B	B	C	D
C	A	C	X

X	X	X	X

In this addition of four numbers, each letter takes the place of a different digit, but an error has crept in. One of the letters is incorrect. Can you tell which one?

85. Practical Trisection

In the nineteenth century, no one could have predicted the technical arsenal we have at our disposal today for drawing curves or constructing the most complex geometric figures. But the mathematicians of the last century were not wholly unequipped. They had the so-called jointed devices. Their curious combinations of arms, joints, and sliding parts were used to partition line segments and angles, inverse circles, and extract the roots of quadratics. Here, for example, is the rhomboid invented in 1871 by Roberts for bisecting angles. The two longer limbs are of equal length, as are the shorter ones. Can you rediscover a similarly simple device for trisecting angles?

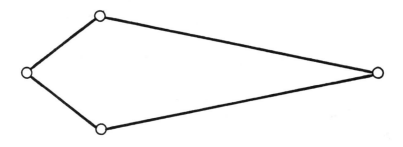

86. The Bandbox

Let us give the name "bandbox" to a solid parallelepiped constructed by gluing together two cubes. We shall accept only those constructions in which each bandbox contacts the rest of the construction in at least one whole surface (rectangular or square). Given that definition, there are, in fact, only two constructions that can be made with two bandboxes. How many can be made with three?

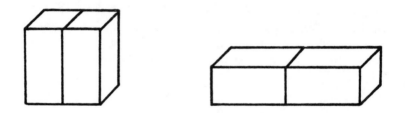

87. A Multicolored Chessboard

If one sets out to color the squares of a chessboard, how many different colors does it take to make it possible to place the king anywhere on the board without his being able to link two squares of the same color by one move?

88. Breaking the Chain

Consider a surveyor's chain made up of 23 links. How many links must one open in order to have a set of segments that can be combined (by relinking) to form all lengths between 1 and 23?

89. What's It Good For?

This apparatus can be used to solve a definite geometric problem. How does one use it, and what is the geometric construction involved? Let us specify that the curve is a circle centering on c and that $ab = bc = cd$. The apparatus is as useful as the length of the vertical arm.

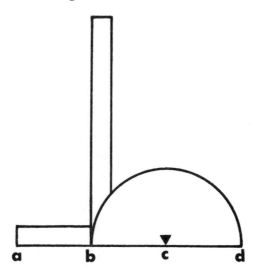

90. Reversible Magic

A numerical palindrome is a number that can be read backward or forward without changing it (e.g., 22, 747, or 5473672763745). Let us take the first twenty-five numerical palindromes starting with 11. Is it possible to construct a magic square with these; that is, a 5 × 5 square in which all the rows and columns, as well as both diagonals, add up to the same number?

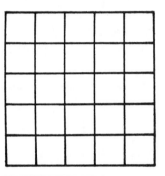

91. A Cross and a Square

This unique cross has an unusual property: it can be cut into eight pieces that can be reassembled into a square. Can you find a way to do that?

92. The Finishing Touch

Two players confront each other over a ticktacktoe board containing nine empty squares. Each player in turn fills in a number of squares with x's, either along one row or down one column, but not both. The squares he fills in do not need to be contiguous. The winner is the one who fills in the last square.

Given these rules, is it possible for one player to be sure of winning, and if so, which player?

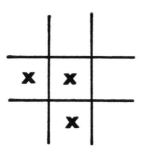

93. Back to Trisection

Let us return to trisecting an angle. One of my readers has noted that the apparatus described in problem 89 cannot be used for all angles, whatever the length of its movable arm. Also, he proposes another device that will work for all angles. It has seven arms and six hinges. Can you reinvent the gadget?

94. The Symmetrical Cross

Let us go back to the cross in problem 91 with the same aim of cutting it up to produce a square, but this time with a different condition.

Instead of trying to find the smallest number of pieces, we must try to make a square out of symmetrical pieces. Can that be done?

95. Century Sundays

January 1, 1978, fell on a Sunday. That being the case, what day will it fall on at the start of the next century? As a more general consideration, what is the probability that the centuries of the Gregorian calendar commence on Sunday?

96. To Have or Not to Have

You are playing bridge, and when the deal is made, each player has thirteen of the fifty-two cards. Which is the more probable of the following two distributions: (1) that you and your partner hold all the red face cards and all the lower cards that are multiples of 3, or (2) that you and your partner hold none of these cards?

97. The Area of the Slice

Is it very difficult to determine areas that are bounded by curved lines? Can you calculate the area of this one, defined by two quarter circles crossing each other as shown in the diagram. They have the same radius and are centered on two sides of a square. The evaluation of the shaded sections should not take more than a few lines of calculation.

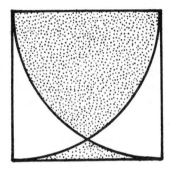

98. Integral Triangles

The right-angle triangle is familiar to every student, and the ones that have solutions in whole numbers (3, 4, 5; 5, 12, 13; etc.) are a joy to fledgling mathematicians, not least because their areas can also be expressed by whole numbers.

Is it possible to maintain these attractive properties without the right angle? In doing so, we would maintain the requirement of sides measurable by whole numbers but add a new property: the sum of the sides must be equal to the area of the triangle. Can this be done? If so, show how to find some of these triangles.

99. Vases

One has two vases with capacities of 3 and 5 pints, respectively, both filled with water. Without the help of another container and by simply pouring water from one vase to another, one wishes to end up with 4 pints of water in a third vase of more than 4 pints that was empty at the outset. What is the required capacity of the third vase?

100. Writer's Cramp

A writer is beset by a curious difficulty. The closer he gets to the end of his work, the slower he writes. When he begins a piece of work, his daily output is proportional to the number of pages remaining to be written. Thus, for a certain book, it takes him ten days to write the first page and fifty days to write the last.

What is the length of the book, and how many days does it take for him to write it? (The remaining number of pages is rounded out each time to the nearest integer.)

101. Lining Up Blacks and Whites

Let us follow up on problem 76, which distributes twenty-one points in fourteen alignments of two white and two black points each, but without symmetry. Can you find a symmetrical solution?

102. More Alignments

Let us go further with the alignment of black and white points (problems 76 and 101). With only one additional point—making twenty-two all told—see if you can create twenty-one alignments of two white and two black points each.

103. Trisection in the Enlightenment

Among the preceding puzzles (89 and 93), several devices for trisecting the angle have been described. Following their publication, one puzzle fan wrote to me to point out that the history of such inventions does not date back to the nineteenth century, as recent publications on the subject would lead one to believe, but can be found as early as the eighteenth century. The Marquis de l'Hôpital found a solution to this technical problem, which was published posthumously in 1720 in a work entitled "A Treatise on the Analysis of Conic Sections and their Importance in Solving Determinate and Indeterminate Problems." His problem VI proposes to "divide any given angle into any odd number of equal parts by means of a mathematical instrument." This involved a device that could be immediately used for trisection. Next, with a slight modification, it could be used to divide the angle into five parts, into seven parts, etc.

Can you reconstruct this device, which was constructed out of jointed or sliding rods?

104. The Odds on the White Card

I shall place three cards in a hat. One is white on both sides, the second is red on both sides, and the third is white on one side and red on the other. I draw a card at random, and without looking at it, place it on a table. When I look at it now, I see that the side that is face up is white. And I deduce from that that there is one chance in two, or even money, that it is either the first card or the third. I bet you four dollars to three dollars that the other side of the card is white. Which of us has the better bet?

105. Pi in an Unfamiliar Context

Study the three shaded lunes. A fan has trapped π within them. In fact, it is possible to cut up remaining portions of the circle into six pieces that can be used to create a regular hexagon that, in turn, in a familiar cutting process, yields a square. It is equally possible to cut out six pieces that can be reassembled into a rectangle in which the sides are in the relation $1\frac{1}{2}/\sqrt{3}$.

How can this be done?

106. Toward Unity

0.8461538461538 . . .
and
0.1538461538461 . . .

are two repeating decimals in which the same series of digits repeat indefinitely. If one adds up each corresponding pair of digits, one obtains a series of 9s. Can one deduce from this that the sum of the two numbers is exactly 1?

107. An Accidental Ellipse

In our everyday life we seldom encounter ellipses. It is not a widespread geometric figure as compared to the omnipresent circle. And if we do not see ellipses very often, we draw them even less.

There exists, however, in many homes a simple device (not used for cooking) that under certain circumstances can produce an ellipse. Although that is by no means its normal function, if this device breaks down through an accident, almost all of its points will individually describe a portion of an ellipse.

What is the device, and what is the accident?

108. Your Basic Boat

Ordinarily, a boat makes headway by acting against something else: against the water if it is propelled by oar or by screw, against the wind and water if it uses a sail, or against the ground if it is towed. Now, is it possible for a boat to move ahead without acting on anything outside itself? Think of yourself in a boat that is entirely enclosed in still water with no current and no wind. Would you be able to make it move?

109. Points and Lines

This figure represents the present record achievement to date in the alignment of twenty-one points: eleven alignments of five points are represented. But one notices at once a defect in the arrangement: there are four unused intersections. They do not contain any point of a sort that would complete the perfection of the whole. One could surmise the possibility of doing better, and this, in fact, has been achieved: a new plane figure of twenty-one points has been discovered that shows two improvements: (1) there are twelve alignments of five points, and (2) all the intersections are employed.

What is that arrangement?

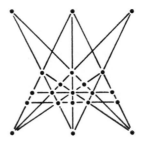

110. Squaring the Square

If the quadrature of circles must be discarded as a valid mathematical problem, at least the problem of combining squares is within our reach. In spite of one's first reactions, it is literally possible to combine two squares to produce a third. Can you show how to do it?

111. The Missing Token

A child who has been given ten tokens marked 0, 1, 2, 3, 4, 5, 6, 7, 8, and 9 announces that he has lost one. His father does not know the number of the missing token, but he is an able logician and engages his son in the following dialogue:

Father: Can you divide the remaining tokens into three groups that add up to the same number?

Child: Yes.

Father: Can you also divide these into four groups that add up to the same number?

Child: Yes.

Father: Then I can tell you the missing token.

Which token is missing?

112. Quadrature and Dissection

The task of juxtaposing two squares to form a third (proposed in puzzle 110) was achieved there by arithmetic. In giving the solution, I expressed a doubt as to the existence of a geometric solution. But this did not discourage one of my readers from finding one. This reader had a completely valid approach: "to juxtapose two squares to form a figure susceptible to being cut up into pieces that would then form a third square." (The two squares of the joined figure here are of any dimensions.)

How many cuts are necessary to produce the pieces to form a third square?

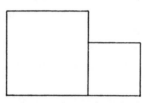

113. An Uneasy Cryptogram

The following message was enciphered by a relatively simple method, but the plaintext has an unusual feature that may cause you trouble. See if you can decipher it.

> XCWXI RQJWJ KRYQS ZIQMQ CXCTX
> VDSDS ZHDQS WJHOX CVJDS AXBRD
> KJXJW QTQYQ KCJOQ XHQCT QMXIF
> DUVHQ IIXCX JIBDK JWJWX IMQIY
> QSZIU XHIJM QHCXC VDUTH KVQTT
> XSJXD C.

114. Roots

Pocket calculators are now ubiquitous in the office and the home, although most are limited to the simplest arithmetic operations. However, it is possible to extract square roots quite quickly even with a calculator that does not have a square-root function. How can you use that device to find square roots with a minimum of trial and error?

115. The Triangulation of the Triangle

In reflecting upon the problem of the quadrature of the square (cutting two juxtaposed squares to make one square from the resulting pieces; see puzzle 112), one of my readers discovered an intriguing related problem. The median of any triangle is cut to form two triangles of equal areas. How can one be cut to obtain pieces that can reconstitute the other?

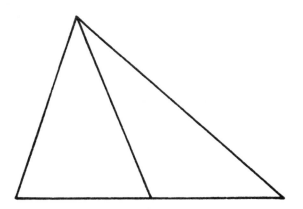

116. Travels on the Hexagon

Can you find the twelve ways of joining the apexes of a hexagon by a continuous sequence of straight lines that form a closed figure and do not pass through any apex more than once?

117. A Bailout Fee

Because of a mistake, a well 20 yards deep has been contaminated. Formerly empty, it is now filled with fuel oil. A workman undertakes to empty the well by means of a pail with a rope and pulley. In that way he is able to lower the level of the oil 1 yard at a time. His charge is $400. If he stops work halfway through (i.e., at the end of 10 yards), how much is he owed?

118. A Prize Hamster

A researcher in an intelligence-testing institute came in to his laboratory one day with a hamster that had been trained by his children. It shattered every record for negotiating a maze. He had no trouble in selling it to a colleague for $425. The latter taught the hamster additional skills and sold it for $470 to a third party, who proceeded to sell it to another for $535. That person sold it for $594 to someone else, who sold it for $716 to someone else, who sold it for $802. If this last buyer intends to pass it on to someone else, how much will he ask for it?

119. The Women Man the Oars

Crossing a river is an old chestnut of recreational mathematics. In a general way, it involves crossing in a boat that seats fewer people than want to cross. Another requirement, which is more logically than socially appealing, is that none of the husbands is willing to let his wife be in the company of another man, either in the boat or on shore, without his being present.

After reading such a problem (58), a woman wrote in to express the regret that (quite apart from the outmoded jealousy) the women were not deemed capable of managing the boat themselves.

To meet this objection, here is a problem in which the jealousy is still a factor but in which one woman, even by herself, is able to row the boat across. Four couples are on one bank. How many crossings will it take to transport everyone to the other bank in a boat that cannot hold more than three persons?

120. Breaking Up a Year

Let us start with 1980; $1979 \times 1 = 1979$ is the smallest number one can find that is the product of two nonnegative integers, the sum of which is 1980.

Turning this around, what is the largest number you can obtain as the product of two whole numbers that add up to 1980?

121. Protagoras at the Bar

The paradox of Protagoras and his pupil is a classic of logic. As a teacher of law, the great sophist once accepted unusual terms of payment from one of his students: he would waive payment until the student won his first suit.

As it turned out, the student did not practice law upon completing his studies and therefore neither lost nor won a suit. And he did not pay Protagoras for his lessons.

On these grounds Protagoras initiated a suit in order to force the student to pay up, and in this legal action each side took an impeccably logical position: Protagoras argued that if the student lost the case, he would have to pay, since that was the object of the suit, but if the student won, he would still have to pay, because that was the requirement of his contract.

The student argued that if he lost the case he would not have to pay, since those were the terms of the contract, but if he won his case, he would not have to pay, because that was the decision of the court.

What ought Protagoras to have done in order to get paid?

122. Squaring Polygons

The art of cutting up geometric figures and then reassembling the pieces into different figures is an ordinary source of inspiration for puzzle lovers. The goal is the traditional one of the mystique of geometry: to produce a square. By now almost all the classical geometric figures have been explored, and it remains to deal with less commonplace ones. For example, take the figure in the diagram. Can you cut it into eight pieces that can be assembled into a square?

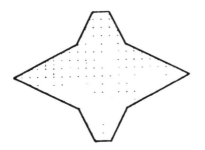

123. Drawing the Line

To retrace a geometric form without lifting the pencil off the page or crossing the same line twice is a well-known diversion for the aficionado of geometric puzzles. Here is a real stumper. It is possible to traverse this diagram not only without breaking the two rules but also by ending up at the starting point. The solution is systematic and is applicable to all multiplications of the original figure. Can you find it?

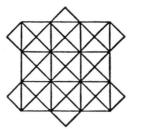

124. A Band of Five Squares Creates Another Square

This band made up of five contiguous squares is easily cut into five pieces that can be reassembled into a square. The solution is given below.

The symmetry of this result is very appealing, but it conceals an even better solution: to cut the band into as few as four pieces that can be assembled into a square. How is that done?

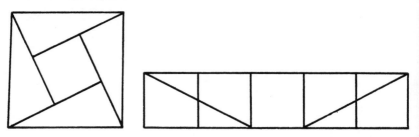

125. The Fifth Power

The ubiquity of calculators in our everyday life relegates number theory increasingly to the researches of experts or the diversions of amateurs. Let us enjoy the fact. Can you demonstrate a property of numbers that is as surprising to those who have forgotten it as to those learning it for the first time: the difference between the fifth power of a number and the number itself is divisible by five. Can you prove in other terms that $n^5 - n$ is a multiple of five?

126. A Line to Follow

Certain problems of recreational mathematics sum up the nature of scientific thought in an astonishing way, when one considers its conflicting opinions and its unexpected solutions. That is certainly the case with problem 123, *Drawing the Line*.

First phase: someone proposes a problem that involves tracing a figure without raising the pencil from the paper or doubling back and at the same time ending at the starting point. Second phase: some readers think they can show that this is impossible. Third phase: a solution is published that fits the rules. Fourth phase: someone demonstrates that the problem is childishly simple, since he has solved it and now wishes to add the constraint of never crossing a line.

Can you solve this amended version of the problem?

127. A Tricky Division

When one-quarter of a square is removed in the form of a piece that is itself a square, what is left of the original square can be divided into four equal and superimposable regions. This is a well-known mathematical puzzle that taxes the ingenuity of anyone encountering it for the first time. But don't even try to solve it; the figure below gives you the solution. Suppose, however, that the part removed is in the shape of a triangle. In that case, how would you divide what is left of the square into four equal and superimposable regions?

128. Unlisted Numbers

A telephone company assigns to its customers all the numbers composed of six digits, but in order to avoid a certain type of mistake it excludes the numbers that contain the digits 12 in any two consecutive positions. How many possible telephone numbers will have to be eliminated on this account?

129. No Way to Make a Square

11
111
1111
11111

Intuitively, we feel that in the above sequence of numbers composed entirely of 1s there are no squares of integers. But can you prove that conjecture?

130. A Primary Law

For every prime number p greater than 3, there exists a whole number m such that $p^2 = 24m + 1$. Is this something profound or trivial? How is it accounted for?

131. Ten Digits for One

The jungle of integers can be explored by the amateur mathematician. He may, as he chooses, either arm himself with the weapons of logic or take pleasure in dealing with phenomena beyond his comprehension by merely guessing them and experimenting with them empirically. Here is a situation that is well suited to either of those two approaches.

$$9 = \frac{57,429}{6,381}$$

Nine is expressed here as a fraction containing all the integers from 1 to 9 taken one at a time. If one admits 0 in order to have all ten digits, it is possible to represent 9 by at least six fractions, although purists may find they stop at three. How many of these expressions can you find?

132. Inside Out

In connection with problem 123, which consists of tracing a closed straight line without a crossing, an interesting question can be raised: the closed curve of every solution defines an inside area and an outside one. Under this condition, is each of the forty-two triangles of the figure always on the inside, is it on the outside, or does its position vary with the particular solution?

133. Raindrops Are Falling . . .

If you have to go somewhere on foot on a rainy day, will you get less wet if you run, will you intercept more raindrops that way, or does it make no difference how fast you go? I wonder about that question every time there's a shower without attempting to deal with it mathematically. It's not a good time to cope with the problem, and as soon as the sun comes out, I tend to forget about it.

One of my readers, however, has attacked the problem. In his reasoning, he represents the human body by a parallelepiped, which for practical purposes is an acceptable approximation. What is the result?

134. Remarkable Quadratures

In problem 110 we juxtaposed the squares of whole numbers in order to produce other squares. Thus, 16 and 81 form 1681, which is the square of 41. One of our colleagues has gone further in this direction in exploring all possibilities up to a billion and itemizing 119 solutions (obtained with the aid of a programmable pocket calculator). He has discovered some extraordinary numbers, one of which is $5,184,729 = 2277^2$, formed by $5184 = 72^2$ and $729 = 27^2$. Can you find another that is a square that can be decomposed in two different ways in the juxtaposition of squares? ($x^2 = A^2B^2 = C^2D^2$)

135. Möbius and His Better Half

Everyone is able to construct or to visualize a Möbius band by cutting a uniform strip of paper and then giving it a half turn before joining the extremities. It is easy to cut this band into two equal parts, either along a line that joins the two sides and opens it or by a central cut that leaves two bands of the same length intertwined.

But how does one obtain two parts of equal area in a continuous straight line along the paper that only touches one edge once?

136. Quadruple Quadrature

"Algebraic" quadrature continues its evolution (see problem 134). In this realm—seemingly not very mathematical—the aim is to juxtapose the squares of integers in order to create other such squares. We have already obtained some startling results. Now we endeavor to go further by finding four squares that will create a fifth square if juxtaposed. Can you find the number x such that $x^2 = A^2B^2C^2D^2$, where the squares are juxtaposed but not multiplied and where A^2B^2 and C^2D^2 are also squares.

137. Something New About Nines

Nine is a remarkable number: it is the only integral square composed of odd digits (digit) only. Every other square (to base 10) contains at least one even digit. Can you find a proof for the last statement? Is it possible to prove it by generalizing the proof for a property of numbers composed of the digit 1 (see problem 129)?

138. The Trisection of Pappus

We have already encountered the trisection of the angle in connection with the devices of the eighteenth and nineteenth centuries, which were invented to perform that geometric task automatically. But the construction of one-third of a given angle is far more ancient than that, since Archimedes and Pappus found a way of achieving this (not, of course, with compass and straightedge alone) before our era.

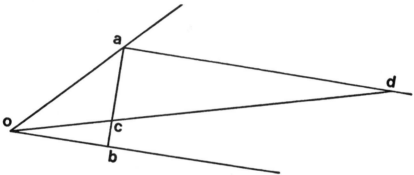

In this construction, attributed to Pappus, an arbitrary distance *oa* is marked on a side of the angle. The line *ab* is perpendicular to the other side, and *ad* is perpendicular to *ab*; *od* is such that *cd* = 2*oa*, which could not, of course, be done using only a compass and straightedge. Why is *boc* one-third the angle *oab*?

139. Archimedes Cuts It Up

Twenty-three centuries before our time, Archimedes played at Tangram (the cut-up square below), a puzzle supposedly of Chinese origin. In Archimedes' version of the game, the goal is to cut up a square into fourteen elements, each of which is in a rational relation to the whole figure.

In Archimedes' solution (below), what is the relation of each piece to the whole?

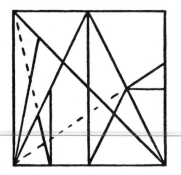

140. Tails I Win

Two contestants take turns tossing a coin. The first one to toss tails wins. Of course, it's obvious that the one who tosses first has a greater chance of winning than his adversary. But what, in fact, are their respective chances exactly?

141. The Barrier of Thirst

The desert march under the conditions imposed has been made with increasing efficiency in the solutions provided in problems 1, 40, and 80. Each time progress has been made by discarding another prejudice. This is no time to abandon such a promising course. As the result of conquering an additional prejudice—more serious than the earlier ones—the supply of water necessary is no longer eleven and one-half days but rather nine and one-half days.

How is that possible?

142. Regrouping the Pieces

Problem 139 also entails three additional puzzles that are not as simple as they may seem at first glance. How can you regroup the pieces, without changing their positions, into different parts of the square representing:
   1) three equal integers;
   2) three consecutive integers;
   3) the first eight numbers and 12?

143. A Square for a Compass

When you are without a ruler, a compass can by itself be used to make a number of geometric constructions. Indeed, one of the most famous achievements along that line is to locate the center of a given circle—already drawn. For the present, let us attempt something not quite so difficult. Using only a compass, see if you can draw a circle and then determine on its circumference the four apexes of a square.

144. Words and Numbers

It is easy to express numbers in terms of letters. All you have to do is spell them out: 1 becomes ONE, etc. But how does one express words by numbers in such a way that every word has one and only one numerical equivalent and is easy to decipher? One solution is to use the numbers of an even pair of digits in such a way that each two-digit section of the number is a letter of the alphabet:

$$ART = 011820$$
$$POT = 161520$$

Would you be able to come up with other ways of doing these and in particular some of the techniques logicians use to express words by numbers and explore the limits of language?

145. Words, Numbers, and Sentences

Following up on the last problem (144), can you find a way of extending the procedure described there for associating a number with a word to an unambiguous way of associating a number with a sentence (composed of words)?

146. A Triangle in a Square

The equilateral triangle is second only to the square as a perfect figure in the planes. Does one give sufficient thought to the possibility of inscribing the former in the latter? Given a square, what is the length of a side of the smallest equilateral triangle that can be inscribed in it?

147. Mysterious Powers

1 2 8 9 0 6 2 5

is a sequence of digits that imparts very special arithmetic properties to numbers terminating in that way. If you are told that these properties involve powers, can you discover what they are?

148. Superior Antimagic

Strengthened by the experience of solving problem 16, let us proceed to the sixth degree of antimagic.

Can you construct a square of thirty-six places that contain the first thirty-six integers placed in such a way that the sums of the six rows and the six columns and the two diagonals are consecutive numbers?

149. Coupled Couples

Let us explore a variation of the "river crossing," problem 119.

Once again we shall accept the constraints imposed by the antiquated passion of jealousy. Six couples are preparing to cross a river in a boat that can take only five persons at a time. Furthermore, no husband will allow his wife to be unaccompanied by him either on the boat or on the shore in the presence of one or two other men. Given these conditions, how many crossings are required?

150. No Holds Barred

The desert to travel in remains the same, and the conditions of the trip are identical with those in problem 1. But now you must perform the feat not with 20, 14, 11½, or 9½ days' worth of water; you must reduce the supply by several more days' worth. You will find that this optimal solution was hidden by an inherent prejudice far stronger than that which you had to deal with in the previous solution.

SOLUTIONS

1. Water in the Desert

The mission can be accomplished by enlisting three companions and setting out as a foursome with a twenty-day supply of water all told.

At the end of the first day, there will remain only a sixteen-day supply of water. One of your companions returns to the starting point, carrying with him a one-day reserve of water and leaving you a fifteen-day supply of water to carry on as a threesome.

At the end of the second day, you will have a twelve-day supply of water. A second companion returns to the starting point with a two-day supply of water, leaving you with a ten-day supply to make the trip as a twosome.

At the end of the third day, you will have an eight-day supply of water, and your last companion makes the trip back to the starting point with a three-day supply of water, leaving you a five-day supply. That will allow you to make the one-day march to your destination, plant the flag, and make the four-day trip back to the starting point.

Did you discover this solution? That's fine, but it's far from the best one. Problem 40 will ask you to reduce considerably your consumption of water.

2. Pure Reason

In 7 seconds the train passes by a stationary observer, or, in other words, travels its own length. To traverse the length of the station means to travel the length of the station and its own length. Thus, the train travels the length of the station (alone) in $26 - 7 = 19$ seconds. In 1 second it travels $380 \div 19 = 20$ meters. In one hour it travels 72 kilometers. Since it travels its own length in 7 seconds, that amounts to $7 \times 20 = 140$ meters.

3. *The Age of His Digits*

Although it is possible to solve this problem in a lengthy and roundabout way, there is a simple and elegant solution based on congruences.

Any number and the sum of its digits will both leave the same remainder when divided by 9. Therefore, dividing both the year of birth and the age in question by 9 must leave the same remainder. The sum of the two numbers (1898) when divided by 9 must leave a remainder twice as large (in this case 8). Therefore, the age in question is 4 plus a multiple of 9; for instance, 13, 22, 31, etc. The correct solution (22) can be found immediately by trial and error.

One reader has pointed out an ambiguity arising from the fact that one's age changes on one's birthday while the year changes on January 1. Taking that into account, the problem admits of two solutions.

4. The Exchange of Knights

Let us change our way of thinking about the moves of the knights on the twelve squares and imagine them carried out only on the files, the numbers of the squares being assigned to the files. In that way we can untangle the skein and give it a simpler form. In this new model, equivalent to the other, a knight's jump can be considered as a move of one square in one direction or the other.

My proposed solution of twenty-six moves has been bettered by numerous readers. The record minimum is sixteen moves.

Here is the solution:

$$10 - 9 - 4$$
$$2 - 9 - 10$$
$$12 - 7 - 2$$
$$1 - 6 - 7 - 12$$
$$11 - 6 - 1 -$$
$$4 - 9 \qquad -$$
$$3 - 4 - 11$$
$$9 - 4 - 3$$

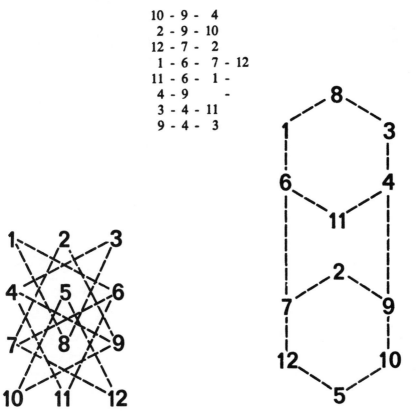

5. *Squaring the Maltese Cross*

This solution achieves in eight pieces what up to now no one could do in fewer than nine.

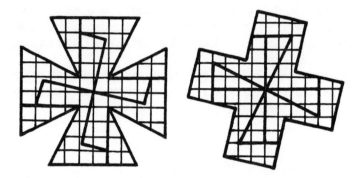

6. *Reconstructing Octagons*

The dimensions of the little octagons must be multiplied by $\sqrt{3}$ in order to obtain the big octagon with three times the surface. It is therefore necessary to produce the hypotenuse of a right-angle triangle with sides $\sqrt{2}$ and $\sqrt{1}$. The rest is inspired trial and error. (See Greg Frederickson, "More Geometric Dissections," *Journal of Recreational Mathematics* [summer 1974].)

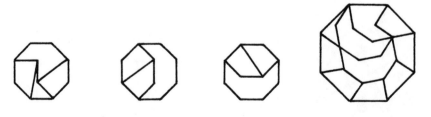

7. Basic Multiplication

Replacing each odd number in the left-hand column by 1 and each even number by 0 is equivalent to expressing the first number in base 2 and reading it from bottom to top. The operations on the right-hand side then represent a multiplication in base 2.

8. A World of Fours

Let us avail ourselves of a little-used mathematical entity; namely, logarithms to the base 4 instead of the more familiar base 10, where $x = \log_4 y$ when $y = 4^x$. Then we can write:

$$- \log_4 \left\{ \log_4 \sqrt{\sqrt{\sqrt{\cdots \sqrt{\sqrt{\sqrt{4}}}}}} \right\}$$

For a given n, the expression contains $2n$ nested square-root signs: something that is possible to do for any given integer n.

This expression is thus equivalent to:

$$- \log_4 \left\{ \log_4 4^{(1/2)^{2n}} \right\}$$

$$= - \log_4 \left(\frac{1}{4} \right)^n = n$$

(See A. P. Domoryad, *Mathematical Games and Pastimes* [Pergamon Press, 1963].)

9. Circular Uncertainties

The third method of calculation proposed by Joseph Bertrand consisted in starting, for reasons of symmetry, with an intersection of the chord with the circle and the angle between the chord and the tangent. The chord must lie within one of the three angles of 60°. Therefore, the probability must be ⅓.

Actually, one knows now that such a problem is not defined until one has specified precisely the stochastic variable, which was not done in the statement of the problem. The three methods of solution refer to three types of experiment and therefore to three different variables:

1) The distance of the chord from the center
2) The angle between the chord and the tangent
3) The position of the midpoint of the chord

Dr. R. J. Denichou has proposed a fourth method of calculation that is equally contradictory. Let us assume a basketful of all the straight lines able to serve as chords, of lengths ranging from 0 to d (the diameter). Those that are suitable have a length falling between $\frac{\sqrt{3}}{2}d$ and d. The probability is therefore $\frac{2 - \sqrt{3}}{2}$. To explore this apparent paradox further, see problem 10.

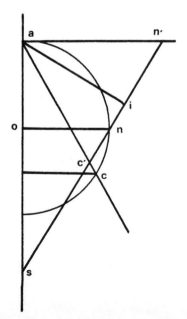

10. The Random Chord

Let ABC be an equilateral triangle and ON a radius perpendicular to OA. S is a point on OA above O. SN intersects AC at C′ and the tangent to the circle at A at N′. Any chord passing through A corresponds to a point on SN′. So the probability that it will be greater than the side of the triangle is $\frac{SC'}{SN'}$. But S may vary, and this "probability" may take any value from 0 (when S = 0) to 1 when S rises.

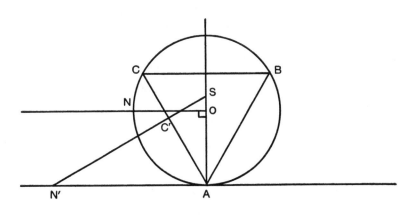

11. What Coincidences?

Every twelve hours the hands of a clock make 1 revolution, 12 revolutions, and 720 revolutions, respectively. The first and the second coincide 11 times and the first and the third coincide 719 times, at regular intervals in each case. But since 719 and 11 are relatively prime, the three cannot align themselves exactly during the twelve hours.

12. Meetings on the Dot

The solution is in the vicinity of an instant when the two slowest hands are superimposed and the third just misses a perfect alignment as it approaches them. The hour and minute hands meet eleven times in twelve hours. At which of these meetings is the second hand closest to them?

The two slower hands coincide at every eleventh part of the clock dial. At the third of these (and its symmetrical counterpart), the second hand is only 1/11 of the dial away from them. The time is 16 4/11 minutes after 3 o'clock.

One obtains the exact solution by moving back the second hand until it coincides with the hour hand, the minute hand being moved back slightly. The hour is that multiple of 1/719 (the coincidence points of hours and seconds) that comes closest to 3/11: namely, 196/719; that is to say, 16 minutes, 16 256/719 seconds after 3 o'clock. The symmetrical solution is 43 minutes, 43 463/719 seconds after 8 o'clock.

13. Steer Metabolism

One can reasonably argue that steers are similar in shape. Now when two solid figures are similar, their areas are proportional to the squares of their linear dimensions, and their volumes, like their weights, are proportional to the cubes. Thus, their areas are determined by the square of the cube root of the weight. The number of calories required is

$$13,500 \times \left[\frac{420}{630}\right]^{2/3} = 13,500 \times \sqrt[3]{\frac{4}{9}} = \text{approximately } 10,300.$$

14. Lightning Calculators

Actually, he does not have to know any of the digits. The only possible answer is 2.

Let us make the calculation with the help of logarithms. The logarithm of a twenty-digit number is 19. . . . The logarithm of its sixty-fourth root is $\dfrac{19\ldots}{64}$. It lies between 0.29 and 0.32. The only integer represented in that interval is 2, or 0.30103.

To take a more direct approach, 10^{64} is a number of 65 digits. $(\sqrt{10})^{64} = 10^{32}$ is a number of 33 digits. $(\sqrt[3]{10})^{64}$ lies between 10^{21} and 10^{22} and is therefore a number of 22 digits. $(\sqrt[4]{10})^{64} = 10^{16}$ is a number of 17 digits. The result is therefore between $\sqrt[3]{10}$ and $\sqrt[4]{10}$. That is equivalent to saying that its cube is less than 10 and its fourth power is greater than 10. The only whole number meeting that condition is 2.

15. Heterogeneous Squares

A square of the second order contains the numbers 1, 2, 3, 4. The smallest sum possible is 3 and the largest is 7. Thus, it is impossible to have six different sums. For the third order, one contributor has reported the existence of 3,120 heterogeneous squares, obtained by selection out of a total of 45,360 squares of order 3 of all possible kinds, generously produced by the computer. Here are some examples:

```
1 2 3        9 8 7        6 5 4
4 5 9        2 1 6        7 2 3
6 8 7        3 4 5        8 1 9
```

16. *Antimagic*

Here is an antimagic square of order 4 in which the sums of the aligned numbers run from 29 to 38:

```
 6   8   9   7
 3  12   5  11
10   1  14  13
16  15   4   2
```

In this square of order 5, the sums run from 59 to 70:

```
21  18   6  17   4
 7   3  13  16  24
 5  20  23  11   1
15   8  19   2  25
14  12   9  22  10
```

17. *Strategic Dates*

The first to play (A) is certain to win if he commits to memory the following sequence of dates: January 20, February 21, March 22, April 23, May 24, June 25, July 26, August 27, September 28, October 29, November 30. In the actual contest A must pick one of these dates as soon as possible.

For obviously, if **A** says November 30, B can reply only with December 30, which lets A win by saying December 31.

If A says October 29, B has only four replies: October 31 and December 29, which allows A to win immediately, or October 30 and November 29, which allows A to win by saying November 30, which wins in two steps as shown above.

By starting with January 20, A is able to keep the upper hand and win.

18. Manual Tactics

The key number is 23: it is the first prime number to be more than five places from the next prime (29). The objective, then, is to be the one to arrive at that cumulative total. In order to do that, the winner must force his opponent to say 13, which can be done by saying 11 and forcing him to say 7 by first saying 5. A wins by starting with 5.

19. Two-Handed Confrontations

In this game, the first jump greater than 10 lies between 113 and 127.

The winning strategy can be deduced as follows: 113 succeeds 103, 107, or 109—therefore, say 101; 101 succeeds 97—therefore, say 89; 89 succeeds 79 or 83—therefore, say 73; 73 succeeds 67 or 71—therefore, say 61; 61 succeeds 53—therefore, say 47; 47 succeeds 37 or 41—therefore, say 31; 31 succeeds 23 or 29—therefore, say 19; 19 succeeds 11, 13, or 17—therefore, say 7. The first player wins by starting his attack with 7.

20. *The Best Bridge*

A problem involving the shortest distance between one point and another can be thought of as an optical problem involving the path of a ray of light. To travel from *a* to *b* on the specified road is obviously the same as going in from *a* to a point *b'* symmetrical to *b* with respect to the bank. One solution would consist of tracing the line *ab'*, cutting the bank at *c*, and then choosing the route *acb*. The solution obtained in this intuitive way can be confirmed in terms of inequalities. Any point (*c'*) other than *c* makes *ac'* + *c'b'* longer and thus *ac'b* longer.

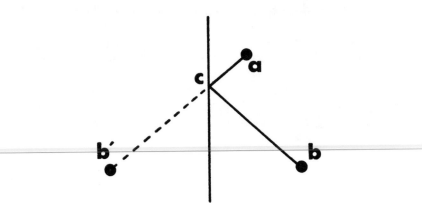

21. The Best Place for the Bridge

Taking the solution to the preceding problem as a guide, let us think of this problem in terms of an appropriate optical analogy. If the canal were a pane of glass and the road a ray of light, the rays to and from the canal would be parallel, but the ray would obviously not cross the bridge perpendicularly to the banks.

To find the shortest path, we establish the auxiliary point a' lying the distance cd from a in the direction of the canal on the perpendicular drawn from a to the canal. From a', draw the straight line connecting a' and b, which crosses b's side of the canal at the point d'. From d' draw the line $d'c'$ crossing the canal perpendicularly back to a's side. The line $d'c'$ determines the best place to put the bridge since it permits the route $ac' + c'd' + d'b$, which is the shortest route from a to b, being equal to the distance $aa' + a'b$ "as the crow flies."

To prove the last equality, we need merely point out that $c'd' = aa'$ (by construction); $ac' = a'd'$ (opposite sides of parallelogram). Therefore, $ac' + c'd' + d'b = aa' + a'b$.

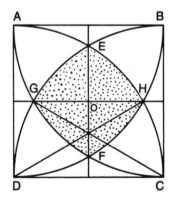

22. *Thrift in Mirrors*

Oddly enough, the answer depends neither on the height of my eyes nor on my distance from the mirror. Whatever the height of my gaze in front of an infinite vertical mirror, (1) the ray of light passing from my eyes to the top of the image of my head strikes the mirror at the midpoint of its (the ray's) trajectory and therefore midway between my eyes and the top of my head; (2) the ray proceeding from my eyes to my feet strikes the mirror midway between my eyes and my feet. All told, the part of the mirror I am actually using is only one-half of my height: say, two feet nine inches.

23. *Multiple Images*

Let a be the angle between the mirrors. The object A has in each mirror an original image A_1 and A'_2. These two produce images in the opposing mirrors: the images A_2 (of A'_1) and A'_2 (of A_1) . . .

Thus, one mirror reflects a sequence of images A_1, A_2, A_2 . . . A_2, located in the planes that form with the bisecting plane the angles a, $2a$, $3a$ . . . na, where na is the greatest term less than or equal to π. If na is exactly equal to π, the two images An and $A'n$ will not overlap and will produce a total of $2n - 1$ images. If a is between $\dfrac{\pi}{1 + n}$ and $\dfrac{\pi}{n}$, one will obtain a total of $2n$ images.

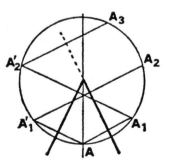

24. A False Proof

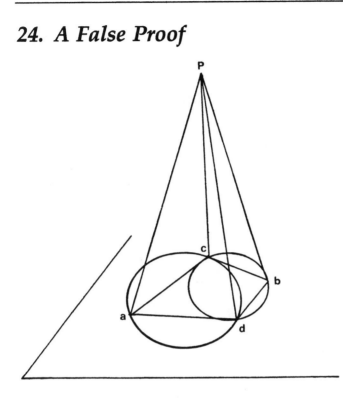

A straight line is not perpendicular to a plane unless it is perpendicular to two distinct and nonparallel lines belonging to the plane. Accordingly, one has to prove that in the two pairs *ca*, *cb* and *da*, *db*, the straight lines are distinct. But that can be the case for only one of these two at the same time.

For clearly, if *p* is projected onto the point *c* of the plane, the center *o* of the sphere having the diameter *ap* is projected onto the plane *ac* in *q*. But *q* is the center of the circle of intersection, and thus *ac* is a diameter. Likewise, *bc* is a diameter of the other circle. Each of these two diameters is tangent to the other circle and thus are perpendicular. Thus, either *acb* or *adb* are not distinct, and either *pc* or *pd* is not perpendicular to the plane.

25. *Visualizing Tetrahedrons*

The triangles *abd, bce, caf,* and *def* all have, taken in pairs, a common side. A point *i*, located above, determines four tetrahedrons fulfilling the condition by means of the surfaces passing through *i*.

Similarly, with a point *j* (not shown) located below and the triangles *klp, lmq, mkn,* and *npq*, one obtains four more suitable tetrahedrons. The common portions of the triangles in the diagram ensure that the group of eight tetrahedrons taken in pairs—but only in pairs—shares a portion of a common surface.

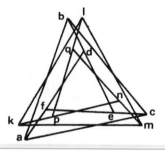

26. *Truth and Brotherhood*

Since each brother does not lie more than once a year, he must tell the truth at least once in the time period of this problem. Thus, the first brother was born either on December 30 or 31. If he was born on the thirtieth he cannot lie on January 1 by saying that he was born on the thirty-first. But if he was born on the thirty-first, he could lie on that day and tell the truth on the next.

The second brother was born either on January 1 or 2. If he was born on the second, he does not have the right to lie on the thirty-first by saying that he was born on January 1. Being born on the first, he tells the truth the first time and lies the second. Thus, the first brother was born on December 31 and the second on January 1.

27. Doubts About Euclid

The most disconcerting thing about this proof is that it makes no use at all of the fact that the two lines are parallel. In reality, when two straight lines are not parallel, the sum of the two angles is greater than two right angles on one side and less than two right angles on the other. But this possibility was missing from the set of hypotheses used in the proof. This possibility also arises with parallel lines without postulating or proving the theorem.

28. The Sum of the Angles

In calling x the sum of the angles of a triangle, we have made the implicit assumption that it is a constant for all triangles. But to begin with, that remains to be proved. It is open to doubt, all the more so because it is obviously false in spherical geometry, for example.

29. Jet Psychology

Vertically, the fall of each drop of water from each hole is governed by the law of distance $= \frac{1}{2}gt^2$. The time periods of the fall of each are t_1, t_2, and t_3, such that $\frac{1}{2}g(t_1)^2 = 1$, $\frac{1}{2}g(t_2)^2 = 2$, and $\frac{1}{2}g(t_3)^2 = 3$. Thus, the times are proportional to $\sqrt{1}$, $\sqrt{2}$, and $\sqrt{3}$.

Horizontally, each drop of water is expelled with a uniform motion with velocity v corresponding to the kinetic energy $\frac{1}{2}mv^2$ equal to the energy lost by the column of water above the hole. Thus, the velocity is proportional to the square root of the height of the water above the hole, and v_1, v_2, and v_3 are proportional to $\sqrt{3}$, $\sqrt{2}$, and $\sqrt{1}$. It follows that the horizontal paths are proportional to $\sqrt{3}$, $\sqrt{2}$, and $\sqrt{3}$. The first and third jets will fall in the same place, closer to the container than the second jet.

30. The Parson and His Sexton

The product of the ages of the parishioners, 2,450, has as its prime factors 1, 2, 5, 5, 7, and 7. Among the nineteen possible triplets (1, 2, 1225), (1, 5, 490) . . . (7, 10, 35), (7, 14, 25), only two have the same sum:

$$5 + 10 + 49 = 64$$
$$7 + 7 + 50 = 64$$

Thus, there are two possible ways of arriving at one age for the sexton. In this case, the oldest parishioner is either 49 or 50. The ambiguity can be resolved only if the parson is 49, so the parishioners are 7, 7, and 50.

31. Revealing Ambiguities

The sum of the two numbers must be an ambiguous one arising out of several different pairs:

$$S = a + a' = b + b' = n + n'$$

Therefore, Simon knows that Paul is confronted with one of the products aa', bb', . . . nn' in such circumstances that the ambiguity of one of them, pp', reveals the solution to Simon. Reciprocally, pp' must correspond to several pairs of which at least two present Simon with ambiguous sums in order for his ignorance not to be revealing to Paul and one of which permits the preceding logical operation.

Let us explain some ambiguous sums beginning with the smallest:

$$6 = 2 + 4 = 3 + 3$$

Neither of the two products, 8 and 9, is ambiguous.

$$7 = 2 + 5 = 3 + 4$$

The products are 10 and 12. Only the second is ambiguous, furnishing Simon with the solution 3 and 4. Let us check this from Paul's point of view. He knows that the product is 12 and can deduce that Simon has the sum 7 or 8 (if the pair is 2 and 6). He reasons that 7 would give Simon sufficient information but 8 would not, for $8 = 2 + 6 = 3 + 5 = 4 + 4$, corresponding to three products, 12, 15, and 16, of which two are ambiguous instead of only one. Therefore, Paul in turn is able to arrive at the answer 3 and 4. The problem calls for only one pair, but others exist—84 and 84, 69 and 96, 98 and 78—that readers have brought to my attention.

32. *An Illegitimate Equilateral Triangle*

To be proved: the triangle formed by the trisectors of an arbitrary triangle is equilateral.

Draw the trisectors of angles B and C, which measure $3b$ and $3c$, A measuring $3a$.

$$a + b + c = 60°$$

Let F and H be such that DFH = FDH = $a + c$ and E and K such that KDE = DEK = $a + b$. One can determine that FDE = $60°$ and that BFD = $a + 60°$. The point D on the bisectors of FBC and ECB is equidistant from BF and CE. As one calculates that DFB and DEC are equal angles, DE = DF and DEF is equilateral. But HF and KE are of course the trisectors of angle A. For note that FK is the bisector of DKE, BF the bisector of DEK, and F therefore the point of intersection of the bisectors of the triangle BK, KE, BX. Since BFH = BFD − HFD = $a + b$, the angle between BX and HF must be $180° − 2d − (180° − 2a − 2b)$, or $2a$. HF is the bisector of BX and KE, and likewise, KE is the bisector of HF and CY.

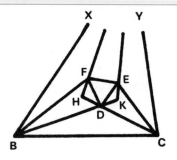

33. Division by Geometry

It is not possible to cover the compartments of a rectangle missing two corners with triple dominoes.

Let us fill in the squares of the rectangle by using three symbols (squares, diamonds, and circles) in such a way that no two neighboring compartments will have the same symbol. Whenever a domino is placed, three different symbols will be covered. To cover the whole figure with dominoes, there would have to be the same number of each symbol. But there are 19 squares, 18 circles, and 17 diamonds.

34. Dismembering One Thousand

The two ways are equally numerous since the odd and even partitions can be placed in one-to-one correspondence. Each even partition—$1,000 = a + b + c + d$—can be paired with an odd partition—$1,000 = (a - 1) + (b - 1) + (c - 1) + (d + 3)$—and each odd partition—$1,000 = a' + b' + c' + d'$—with an even partition—$1,000 = (a' + 1) + (b' + 1) + (c' + 1) + (d' - 3)$. With this one-to-one correspondence, the two sets are equal.

35. *How Many Elevators?*

There are fifteen floor-to-floor connections to be provided within the six intermediate floors, and each elevator provides at most three of these, so *a priori* there are at least five elevators.

This situation is equivalent to incorporating in 15 different triangles the 15 line segments joining the apexes of a hexagon. If the "triangle" 135 is chosen, then the line 4-5 is either bound to 2, which leaves 5-6 unusable, or to 6, which links 3-4 to 2 and leaves 1-4 unusable.

Each triangle, then, must have at least one external side, and only one triangle can have two external sides, for example, 1-2-3. But in that case, 3-4 is bound to 6 and 1-6 cannot belong to any triangle. The partitioning of segments is therefore impossible, and one is forced to use a less economical six-elevator system. For example:

$$
\begin{aligned}
&G\ 1\ 2\ 4\ 7\\
&G\ 2\ 3\ 5\ 7\\
&G\ 3\ 4\ 6\ 7\\
&G\ 1\ 4\ 5\ 7\\
&G\ 2\ 5\ 6\ 7\\
&G\ 1\ 3\ 6\ 7
\end{aligned}
$$

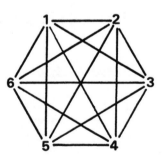

36. The Queen Takes a Walk

The chess queen traverses the board in fourteen moves, as follows:

37. An Attractive Number

If in the three-digit number a,b,c, a is greater than c, then, allowing for the necessary carryovers:

$$a,b,c - c,b,a = a - 1 - c, 9, c + 10 - a.$$

In this expression, it is clear by inspection that the expressions on either side of the constant middle digit 9 add up to 9.

Thus, the three-digit numbers produced by the subtraction $a,b,c - c,b,a$ must have one of the following values: 099, 198, 297, 396, or 495, each one following the other in the sequence of operations of rearrangement and subtraction described in the original statement of the problem. In other words, the numbers on either side of 9 will increase and decrease by 1, respectively. That is because $c + 10 - 9$ will decrease by 1 for successive subtractions and of course $(9 - c + 10 - 9)$ on the other side of 9 will increase by 1 correspondingly.

Thus, the numbers on the left of 9 will increase by 1 at the end of each operation step, and the numbers on the right of 9 will decrease by 1 until the number 495 is reached, at which point that number will repeat indefinitely (since 594 and 495 have the same digits). This theorem can be extended to four digits as well as to numbers in bases other than 10. For four-digit numbers in the decimal system, convergence begins with the number 6174. This algorithm was discovered by the mathematician Kaprekar.

38. If and Only If

Two affirmative statements are linked by "if and only if . . . then": (A) I raise Tom or Dick, or both, and do not raise Harry; (B) I raise Tom, and if I raise Dick, I raise Harry. A and B are both true or both false. A is true if both affirmations joined by "and" are true and false if one of them is false. Since the plan is to raise two of the three employees, A is true only if Tom and Dick are raised. That verifies the first part of B: Tom is raised. But then the second part becomes false: Dick is raised, but Harry is not. A and B cannot both be true. Can they both be false? If Tom and Harry are raised, A is false with respect to the second part. But the first part of B is true, and the second part is equally true, for a false premise is compatible with either a true or a false conclusion.

Finally, if Dick and Harry are raised, A remains false, and B becomes false by virtue of its first part.

Therefore, it is Dick and Harry who get the raises.

39. *Curvilinear Mystery*

In tackling this problem, you must remember the elementary fact that the area of a circle of radius 1 is π. Draw all the additional lines shown in the diagram. The points G and H indicate points of intersection of the quarter circles. The point O is the center of the square ABCD. The two circular segments CGC and DHD are equal to ⅙ circle minus ½ of the equilateral triangles BGC and EDH, respectively, that is, $\dfrac{\pi}{6} - \dfrac{\sqrt{3}}{8}$. By inspection, the area of the two circular segments defined above and the square HOFC equals ¼ circle plus ¼ the circular square

(S) or $2\left(\dfrac{\pi}{6} - \dfrac{\sqrt{3}}{8}\right) + \dfrac{1}{4} = \dfrac{\pi}{4} + \dfrac{S}{4}$, which leads to $S = \dfrac{\pi}{3} - \sqrt{3} + 1$, or approximately 0.31.

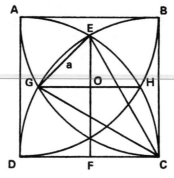

40. *Less Water in the Desert*

It is possible to accomplish the feat by yourself with a fourteen-day supply of water if you are willing to make a number of trips back and forth to place reserve supplies of water along the way.

1) Start with five days of water and leave three of these a day's march from the base.

2) Set out again with five days of water. After one day's walk, take a one-day supply from your reserve, proceed one day further, leave a two-day supply there, and return to the base.

3) Leave with water for four days, take another day's worth at each station on the way. That will enable you to reach your destination and return.

This solution is better than the first, since six fewer days of water are consumed. But in spite of that, it is not the best solution. See problem 80.

41. Superfluous Digits

The three-digit divisor that produces a three-digit number when it is multiplied by 8 has to be a number between 100 and 124, inclusive; 9 is the only number that, when multiplied by such a divisor, produces a four-digit number. Therefore, 9 is the last digit of the quotient.

Since the first subtractions result only in a two-digit number, the first digit of the quotient must be greater than 7. Since it cannot be 9, it is 8. The remaining two digits of the quotients are zeros. Again, because the first subtractions have only two digits, 8 times the divisor must produce a number of at least 990 and that in turn requires that the divisor must be 124. It follows that the division in question is:

$$
\begin{array}{r|l}
10020316 & \underline{124} \\
\underline{992} & 80809 \\
1003 & \\
\underline{992} & \\
1116 & \\
\underline{1116} & \\
\end{array}
$$

42. A Difficult Juncture

At the intersection, let us inscribe a sphere that is contained within both cylinders. Now cut through the planes parallel to the two axes. A calculation of the volume will require the summation of the intersection. Since they are both squares, the planes cutting the cylinders along the generatrices, the inscribed circles are the intersections with the sphere. Since the calculation of the volume of the sphere will be a summation on the circles, the two volumes are in proportion to the areas of the square and the circle:

$$\frac{V}{4 \pi \sqrt{3}} = \frac{4}{\pi}$$
$$V = \frac{16}{3}$$

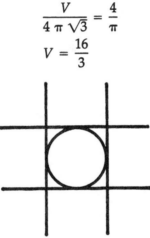

43. Using Your Imagination

The value of the required final digit does not depend on the three-digit number from which it was derived and which I hope you did not bother to calculate. For it is a fact that every integer and its fifth power have the same last digit (i.e., in the units place). Strange as it is, the original three-digit number would have led you to this result one step at a time. It can be easily verified.

44. Father, Son, and Horse

Unless one is careful in considering this problem, it is possible to fall into the trap of believing that the overall time of the trip can be shortened by traveling any part of it at the speed of the horse. If the father and the son are to arrive at their destination at the same time, the person riding cannot average better time than the person walking. If the rider goes faster than the walker, he must wait for him to catch up after he has fallen behind.

In fact, there cannot be a single solution to this problem without supplying what part of the trip each person is allowed to ride. To arrive together in the *shortest* time (7½ hours), the son will have to do all the walking. Doubtless, the father will prefer this solution for other reasons, as well.

45. *Archimedes Trisects the Triangle*

Given an arbitrary angle x, draw a semicircle at 0 with a radius equal to the (arbitrary) distance between two points on a straightedge. A and B represent the points of intersection of the circle with the initial and terminal sides of $\angle x$, respectively. Extend the base of $\angle x$ along the diameter to the left with the straightedge. Now, keeping the edge of the straightedge extending through B, manipulate the straightedge in such a way that one of the marked points lies on the semicircle at some point D and so the other marked point lies on some point C of the diameter. The angle BCA is ⅓ the given angle AOB. Proof: △ CDO is isosceles and $\angle$ DOC = $\angle$ DCO. Then, since the external angle BDO = $\angle$ DCO + $\angle$ DOC = 2BCO, $\angle$ BDO = 2 × $\angle$ DCO. But △ BOD is also isosceles and $\angle$ BDO = $\angle$ DBO. External angle AOB = $\angle$ BDO + $\angle$ DCO or $\angle$ AOB = 2 × $\angle$ DCO + $\angle$ DCO = 3 $\angle$ DCO. Therefore, $\angle$ DCO = $\angle$ BCA = ⅓ $\angle$ AOB.

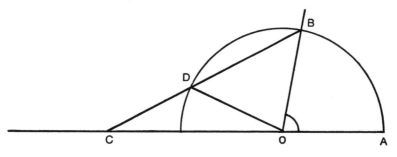

46. Predictable Pain

Instead of focusing on the intervals between the irritations, let us study the abscissas. In this way one obtains 2, 4, 9, 12, 13, 16, 20, 23, 26, 28, 30, 36, 37, 39. If he had but one eyelash behaving normally and growing regularly, we would have an arithmetic sequence. As it is not that, the phenomenon must be a more complex one. Is it possible that there are several eyelashes growing at different rates?

One notices an arithmetic series beginning at the origin, or zero: 0, 13, 26, 39. Thus, the eyelash that was plucked out was able to grow back in 13 days. The other observations, as well, can be rationalized only by separating these into two arithmetic series: one beginning at 2 with constant increments of 7 and one beginning at 4 with constant increments of 8.

The irritation can be produced by three eyelashes growing back in 7, 8, and 13 days.

47. Watch Out for the Train

In the same period of time, the man can escape by running forward the last third of the bridge or backward a third. At that moment, the train has just reached the bridge. If the man is able to escape by running backward, it means that the train covers the whole length of the bridge in the time the man covers the remaining third. Thus, the man runs at one-third the speed of the train, or 15 miles per hour.

48. Knight Moves

A knight's move is either from one file to a contiguous one or from one rank to a contiguous one. From each of the $p - 1$ first files, it can make $q - 2$ jumps to the next column, either up or down. Including its jumps backward, one has $4 (p - 1) (q - 2)$ jumps.

Similarly, from each of the $q - 1$ first ranks it can make $(p - 2)$ jumps to the following rank, making a total of $4 (q - 1) (p - 2)$ jumps. Taken together, we have $4 (q - 1) (p - 2) + (p - 1) (q - 2)$. On the 7×9 rectangle, 328 jumps are possible.

49. Playing with Blocks

This problem is equivalent to solving in terms of positive integers the equation $x^2 + y^2 = (x - y)^3$. Let us begin by creating the equivalent equation $(x - y)^3 - (x - y)^2 = 2xy$. That means that for any cube n^3 that represents the right number of blocks, there are two numbers x and y such that $x - y = n$ and

$$xy = \frac{(n^3 - n^2)}{2}.$$

These conditions for the values of x and y for a given n can be expressed by the quadratic equation

$$x^2 - nx - \frac{(n^3 - n^2)}{2} = 0.$$

Since the discriminant of this quadratic equation is $2n^3 - n^2$ for any number of blocks meeting the conditions of the problem, $2n^3 - n^2$ must be a perfect square. Using this as a test for $n = 1$, $2, 3, \ldots$ one finds that $n = 5$ has the "acceptable" discriminant $250 - 25 = (15)^2$. Solving the quadratic gives $x = 10$. Since y must then be 5, the two squares are 10^2 and 5^2, and the set has 125 blocks.

50. IQ Logic

The fractions can be written in the form

$$\frac{1}{1 \times 5} \quad \frac{1}{5 \times 9} \quad \frac{1}{9 \times 13} \quad \frac{1}{13 \times 17} \quad \frac{1}{17 \times 21}$$

Therefore, the next term could be

$$\frac{1}{21 \times 25} = \frac{1}{525}$$

and the general term is $\dfrac{1}{[1 + 4(n - 1)] [1 + 4n]}$

In order to arrive at the general case for the sum of n terms, we observe that

$$S_1 = \frac{1}{1 + 4} \quad S_2 = \frac{2}{9} = \frac{2}{1 + (2 \times 4)} \quad S_3 = \frac{3}{13} = \frac{3}{1 + (3 \times 4)}$$

In order to confirm our intuition as to this pattern, note that if

$$Sn = \frac{n}{1 + 4n}$$

$$Sn + 1 = \frac{n}{1 + 4n} + \frac{1}{(1 + 4n) [1 + 4(n + 1)]}$$

$$Sn + 1 = \frac{n + 1}{1 + 4(n + 1)}$$

Thus, the sum of thirteen terms is $\dfrac{13}{53}$.

51. *Magic Cubes*

Top part:	10	26	6
	24	1	17
	8	15	19
Middle part:	23	3	16
	7	14	21
	12	25	5
Bottom part:	9	13	20
	11	27	4
	22	2	18

It will be noted that this cube has been filled by a series of identical jumps interrupted by regular deviations. One supposes that the cube reproduces itself identically in all directions and:

a general jump: a step downward to the level below.

after each multiple of 9, a step below.

after each multiple of 3, a step down and to the right toward the bottom.

52. *Three Strokes of the Compass*

On a straight line, *ab* and *ac* are lengths *a* and *b*, respectively. One draws the circle of radius *ac* and determines the point such that *bd* = *ac*. The circle with center *d* has the same radius as the first and cuts the first circle at *e*. The two triangles *eab* and *cae* are both similar and isosceles. Their base angles are equal. Therefore,

$$\frac{ab}{ea} = \frac{ea}{ac}$$

This construction supposedly dates back to the seventeenth century (Thomas Strode).

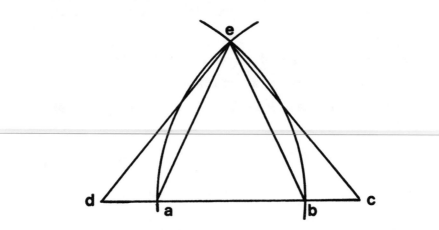

53. To Be Continued

Here are some continuations of the sequence 1, 2, 3, 4, 5:

1) 1, 2, 3, 4, 5, 3, 7, 4, 6, 8, 11 . . .
   U_n is the smallest number the factorial of which is divisible by n.

2) 1, 2, 3, 4, 5, 5, 7, 6, 6, 7, 11, 7, 13 . . .
   U_n is the sum of the prime factors.

3) 1, 2, 3, 4, 5, 6, 7, 1, 2, 3, 4, 5, 6, 7, 8, 2 . . .
   U_n is the smallest number of cubes required to represent n.

4) 1, 2, 3, 4, 5, 6, 7, 8, 9, 10, 11, 12, 13, 14, 15, 1 . . .
   U_n is the smallest number of fourth powers necessary to represent n.

5) 1, 2, 3, 4, 5, 6, 7, 8, 9, 10, 11, 12, 15, 20, 22 . . .
   U_n is a sequence of numbers divisible by each of their digits.

6) 1, 2, 3, 4, 5, 6, 7, 8, 9, 10, 12, 14 . . .
   U_n = numbers that do not have a prime factor greater than 7.

7) 1, 2, 3, 4, 5, 6, 7, 8, 9, 11, 22, 33 . . .
   U_n = palindrome numbers symmetrical with respect to their center.

8) 1, 2, 3, 4, 5, 7, 8, 9, 11, 13 . . .
   U_n = powers of a single prime.

(See N.J.A. Sloane, *A Handbook of Integer Sequences* [New York: Academic Press, 1973].)

54. *Five Folds*

1) *ef* is determined by folding *bc* to *ad*.
2) *g* by making a fold from *d* such that *c* comes down along *ef*.
3) *hi* by making a fold from *g* such that *a* comes down along *ad* and *b* along *bc*.
4) *j* by folding *ic* to *ih*.
5) *jk* by making a fold from *j* such that *d* comes down along *dc* and *a* along *ab*.

ijkc is a square.

And in the triangle *hgd*, *dg* = 1 and *hg* = ½. Thus, $hd^2 = 1 - \frac{1}{4} = \frac{3}{4} = jk^2$.

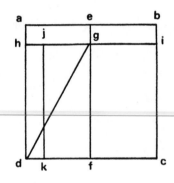

55. Nine Lines Make Twenty-One Triangles

Here is how to make twenty-one triangles with nine straight lines.

56. A Cube of Bricks

Twenty-seven bricks measuring $2 \times 1 \times \frac{1}{2}$ cannot be assembled into a cube $3 \times 3 \times 3$. Let us construct a cube as an assemblage of 27 little cubes $1 \times 1 \times 1$ composed alternately of black-and-white material. Cubes of the same color come into contact only along straight lines.

Now if the bricks are assembled to form a cube, none of them placed at a slant, each brick must be parallel to the edges and occupy as much of the black as white volume.

Therefore, all told, the 27 bricks must produce $13\frac{1}{2}$ white cubes and $13\frac{1}{2}$ black cubes, which is obviously impossible.

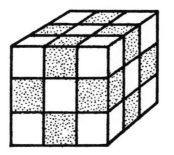

57. Kicking a Goal

Let us assume that the player is at X, an arbitrary point on the sideline. We proceed to draw the circle that passes through X and the two goalposts B_1 and B_2. If the circle retraverses the sideline at a second point X', it makes no difference whether one shoots from X or X': at both points, the angle is the same, since it is contained in equal arcs of the circle. But it is preferable to shoot from any point other than X or X' in the circular segment XX'. (At all these other points, the angle is greater.) X is the optimal point if and only if the circle is tangent to the sideline and does not retraverse it. In that particular case, we can write the square of the distance from the corner of the field C to X in relation to the circle:

$CX^2 = CB_1 \times CB_2 = (35 - 3.66)(35 + 3.66)$ and $CX = 34.81$ meters.

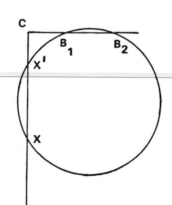

58. Other People's Husbands

Five crossings suffice to transport n couples on a boat capable of carrying $(n - 1)$ persons.

1) $(n - 1)$ wives get in the boat and cross over to the other side.
2) $(n - 2)$ wives stay where they are, and the remaining one brings back the boat.
3) The wife who has done the rowing remains on the original shore to rest up in the company of her husband and one other couple, while $(n - 2)$ husbands take the boat across again to rejoin their wives.
4) One couple returns to the original shore.
5) The remaining three couples make the fifth trip.

59. Sequences and Gaps

The sequence of the divisors of 27720 (i.e., 2, 3^2, 5, 7, 11) is 1, 2, 3, 4, 5, 6, 7, 8, 9, 10, 11, 12, 14, 15, 18 . . . Excluded is the number 13. In the same way, definitions of sequences in the form of groups of numbers that share a common divisor with a given number allow one to exclude any given prime number, at the same time including all the integers that precede it.

One would not suppose it possible similarly to exclude a composite number in the same way. To do that one makes use of the function E (the whole part of a rational number). Thus, for example, 14 is excluded from this sequence, which contains the numbers that come before and after it:

$$U_n = E\left(n + \frac{n}{14}\right)$$

60. Trick Squares

Let us examine four squares about the same point:

A	B
C	D

If A contains a and B contains ab, a multiple of b, it is possible to fill D with b (provided that b and a are relatively prime). But now one cannot fill C, which cannot have a common factor with a or b without having one with ab. Therefore, two squares meeting along a line can never contain a number and one of its multiples, but must contain two numbers of the form ab and ac, where b and c are relatively prime. The first line can therefore take the form:

$$ab \qquad ac \qquad ad \qquad ae$$

and the first column the form:

$$ab \qquad fb \qquad gb \qquad hb \quad \text{etc.}$$

One is led to create a kind of multiplication table of the first eight primes. In order to keep their products as low as possible, the four biggest primes are paired with the four smallest, which yields the solution:

	2	3	5	7
11	22	33	55	77
13	26	39	65	91
17	34	51	85	119
19	38	57	95	113

61. *Circles and Square Roots of Seven*

Let *pq* be the unit length. We can trace these circles:
1) Having center *p* passing through *q*.
2) Having center *q* passing through *p* and intersecting the first at *r* and *m*.
3) Having center *r* passing through *p* and *q* and intersecting the first two at *t* and *s*.
4) Having center *t* passing through *p* and *r* and intersecting the first circle at *u*.

The sought-after length is *su*, for

$$su^2 = ms^2 + mu^2$$
$$= (1 + 1)^2 + (\sqrt{3})^2$$
$$= 4 + 3$$
$$= 7$$

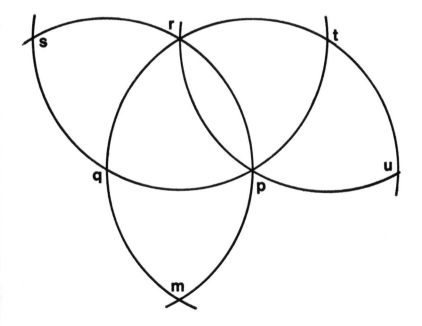

62. *An Adequate Supply of Digits*

Write down all the numbers in a column, one above the other, and line them up on the right-hand side so that the unit digits will be in the same column. Add a line of m zeros along the top containing enough zeros so that each number will have m digits. Accordingly, this table will contain $m(N + 1)$ digits. How many zeros does one have to eliminate?

The numbers from 10^{m-1} to N have none, but there are 10^{m-1} in the left-hand column, 10^{m-2} in the second column, 10 in the next-to-last column on the right, and 1 in the last column.

The total must be $\dfrac{10^m - 1}{9}$ (a number composed of 1s).

That leaves $m (N + 1) - \dfrac{10^m - 1}{9}$ digits.

63. *Pawn Parity*

There is invariably an even number of pawns on the white squares.

Let us assign coordinates to each square running from bottom to top vertically and from left to right horizontally. In the 3 × 3 board, the coordinates of the black squares (1,1), (1,3), (3,1) . . . have both coordinates of the same parity and of different parity from the white squares.

An arrangement of n pawns on different rows and columns can be expressed $(1, y_1)$, $(2, y_2)$ . . . (n, y_n) where the y's are all different. Therefore, the sum $(1 + y_1) + (2 + y_2) + \ldots + (n + y_n)$ is even since it is double the sum of the first n numbers. If one excludes all the parentheses with even sums (i.e., the black squares), the sum of the remaining odd numbers is even, that is, there is an even number of white squares.

64. Trick and Countertrick

The present record is:

A contributor has raised a subtle question: can a square be simultaneously trick and magic? (Can its lines, columns, and two diagonals have the same sum?)

5	22	3	7
2	15	14	9
27	26	33	4
13	21	10	11

65. Squaring a Star

Here is a simple way to cut up the star in order to form a square:

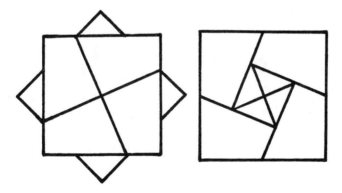

66. *Matchmaking*

The figure shows the 12 ways of connecting five matches that touch each other in at least one extremity; 28 ways have been identified for six matches, 74 ways for seven, and 207 ways for eight.

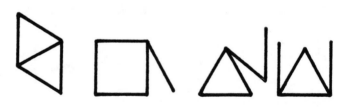

67. Prime Magic

A little experimenting shows that 111 is the smallest sum of three primes summed in the eight required ways.

7	73	31
61	37	13
43	1	67

68. Constructive Folds

The square must be folded in two twice in order to produce the medians EF and GH with the center O.

Next, one refolds AD and BC on EF in order to determine IJ and KL, equidistant parallel lines. The part to the right of EF is folded back, as is the lower part of GH in order to set off angle EOG. That makes it possible to place O on IJ and to fold GM in such a way that GM = GO. One obtains GQ = HP = HN in the same way.

Since angle MGO is 60° and GO = MN = PQ, GMNHPQ is indeed a regular hexagon.

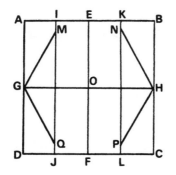

69. Three and Five Make Four

Let us construct a parallelogram on the two axes Ox and Oy at an angle of 60° and divided into equilateral triangles. Ox represents the 5-pint container, empty at O and full at A. Oy represents the 3-pint container B. Let us call C the 8-pint container.

The three possible kinds of decantations are:

1) y remains constant; that is, pouring from C into A or from A into C.
2) x remains constant; that is, pouring from C into B or from B into C.
3) $x + y$ remains constant; that is, pouring from A to B or from B to A.

The aim is to start from O and by means of a broken line to end up at Z. Each segment will traverse the parallelogram. Also, it will always be more efficient to bounce off a boundary line with a symmetrical ricochet (as in billiards) rather than at any other angle.

One can start along either axis. For example, OA-A*e-ef-fg-gh-hl*; or OB-B*j-jk-kl-lm-mn-no-oZ*.

The first solution requires only six operations.

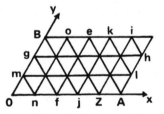

70. The Price Is Right

The prize can be won as follows. Let us suppose that the correct price P happens to be within the $511 range. The price can then be found by making corrections in intervals equal to decreasing powers of 2. Suppose the first estimate is N_1. If that is incorrect, the response N_2 should be:

$$N_2 = N_1 + 256 \text{ if } N_1 < P$$
$$N_2 = N_1 - 256 \text{ if } N_1 > P$$
$$N_3 = N_2 + 128 \text{ if } N_2 < P$$
$$N_3 = N_2 - 128 \text{ if } N_2 > P$$
etc.
$$N_{10} = N_9 + 1 \text{ if } N_9 < P$$
$$N_{10} = N_9 - 1 \text{ if } N_9 > P$$

At the worst, $N_1 - N_{10} = 256 + 128 + 64 + 32 + 16 + 8 + 4 + 2 + 1 = 511$. Thus, one sweeps through the whole range between $N_1 - 511$ and $N_1 + 511$, and the right number is found.

71. Newton's Steers

The key to solving this problem easily is to calculate the amount of grass growing on one acre in one day, as expressed in terms of the surface area of the same amount of grass at the original height. The value for the appropriate constant factor h can be obtained from the two equal expressions for the amount of grass cropped by a steer in a day, as calculated from the preliminary data of the problem.

Thus, if $\dfrac{60 + (12 \times 60h)}{75 \times 12} = \dfrac{72 + (15 \times 72h)}{81 \times 15} = 1\frac{1}{3}$, then h must equal $\frac{1}{12}$.

If one allows for the growth of the grass, cropping a field of 96 acres in 18 days is the equivalent of cropping $96 + (18 \times 96h) = 240$ acres. At the rate of $1\frac{1}{3}$ acres per steer per day, 100 steers would be needed.

72. *Sixteen Equals Four Times Fifteen*

73. *Truncated Cubes*

If a cube is truncated at one apex, only one axis will survive: the axis of symmetry of order 3 perpendicular to the equilateral triangle.

If it is truncated at two apexes, there will remain one axis of order 3 and three axes of order 2.

If it is truncated at four nonadjacent axes, there will remain three axes of order 2 (the original axes of order 4) and four axes of order 3.

74. Leaping Counters

The situation is greatly simplified by rearranging the positions in such a way that they are next to each other if they are linked by a simple jump. In that case, the displacements will consist of moving to an adjacent numbered position. The counters are all on their original positions. One sees that they cannot leap over one another and can only achieve the circular permutations on 1 4 2 3:

a d b c, d b c a, b c a d, and *c a d b*. This gives for 1 2 3 4: *a b c d, d c a b, b a d c, c d b a*.

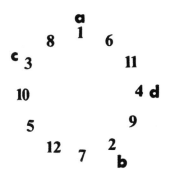

75. Trickery and Magic

This square is both magic insofar as its rows, columns, and diagonals add up to 90 and antitrick insofar as the numbers that are adjacent vertically or horizontally are relatively prime and have a common divisor when they touch each other at an angle.

Are there larger magic and antitrick squares? Are there magic and trick squares in which the numbers that touch diagonally are relatively prime and have a common divisor if they touch at an angle?

3	32	39	16
40	9	14	27
21	34	33	2
26	15	4	45

76. *Black and White Dots*

The numbers 21 and 14 are multiples of 7, suggesting an intersecting heptagon for constructing the following solution of 21 dots in 14 alignments of two black dots and two white dots.

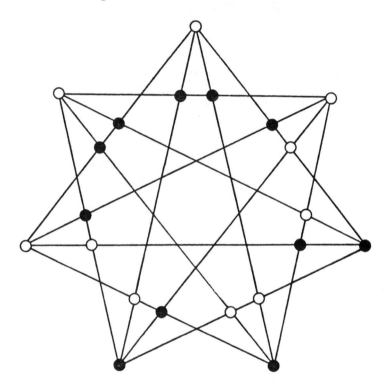

77. *Christmas Dinner*

By a point on a circle, let us represent each brother, and let us join each to the position of his wife by a chord. If we systematically explore all the ways of arranging the six chords, we can count nine different figures, each of which can be permutated by rotating the arrangement of the chords.

The first figure, the figure itself and its mirror image, gives two arrangements for the wives. Equally, the second figure gives two arrangements. The following figures give, respectively, 4, 6, 6, 12, 12, 12, and 24 arrangements, yielding a total of 80. Thus, the possibilities will be exhausted in 40 years.

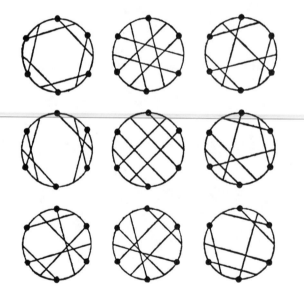

78. Flawless Cubes

Here is an assemblage of tricubes in which no pair of tricubes overlap the same vertical or horizontal layer.

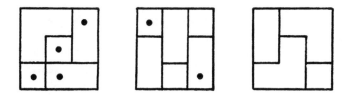

79. What Times Are They?

There does not appear to be an algebraic solution that eliminates trial and error. It is simpler, therefore, to imagine (or actually use) two strips of paper divided by vertical lines into intervals of five units and four units, respectively. In testing the seven positions from second to second that do not allow the chimes of the two clocks to differ more than three seconds from second to second one finds thirteen strokes from five positions and in each instance for nine o'clock. One can assume that it is nine o'clock and overlook any divergence in the rates of the clocks.

There is another solution. If one accepts that the two clocks do not have a difference in synchrony of an integral number of seconds, one can consider the possibility of its being eight o'clock for an asynchrony of between two and three seconds.

80. Beyond Thirst

Here is a way of planting the flag by a system requiring only eleven and a half days worth of water. It requires the slight innovation of accepting a solution involving fractions of days.

Let us designate A as the starting point, B a point a quarter of a day's march away from A, C a day and a half away from A, and D the point of arrival. The man carrying the flag leaves with a five-day supply of water of which he leaves a four-and-a-half-day supply at B and then returns to the starting point. He sets out again with a five-day supply; sets aside a one-quarter day's supply at B, and a two-and-a-half-day supply at C before returning. On the return trip he uses one quarter of a day's water at B. The final time he leaves with one and one-half days' water and picks up three and three-quarters at B and one and one-quarter at C. He marches the remaining distance and plants the flag. On the way back, he takes one and one-quarter from C and two and one-quarter from B.

Do you think that this is the best possible solution? Turn to problem 141.

81. Kings, Queens, and Knaves

Let us follow the situation of the first player and suppose that he holds c cards of which f are face cards. The probability of his failing to draw a face card on his first try is $\dfrac{c - f}{c}$, and the probability of his failing on his second try is $\dfrac{(c - 1) - f}{c - 1}$. If one equates the product of those two probabilities to ½, one can calculate that $c = ½ (4f + 1 ± \sqrt{8f^2 + 1})$, but f can take only the values between 1 and 12. Since c and f must be whole numbers, the first player can only have 21 cards, of which 6 are face cards, or 4 cards, of which one is a face card. And the second player must be subject to the same calculations. In order for the third player to have the smallest hand, it is necessary that both of the first two have 21 cards, of which 6 are face cards. And if that is so, the third player can hold no face cards. (See Jacoby and Benson, *Mathematics for Pleasure* [New York: Fawcett, 1973].)

82. *Folding, Folding*

It's easy to determine an octagon by another method of creating folds in a square, if we change dimensions. An octagon of half the size appears when we use folds to join each midpoint of a side to its two opposite angles.

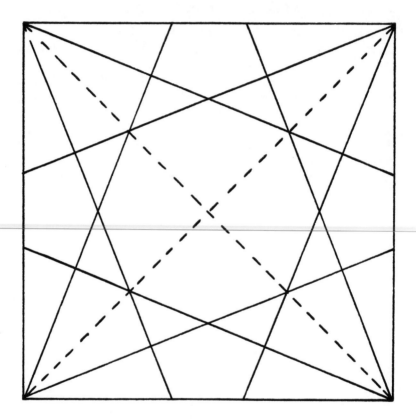

83. Whodunit?

The two last statements of A and C are the most important because they respond to each other and risk contradiction. If A is right when he says that C will tell the truth, C should be believed when he says that A has lied, which is impossible. A is mistaken, therefore, and the last statement of C is not true. For this to be contrary to truth, at least one statement of A must be true. This can only be the first, so B is guilty.

84. A False Unknown

The digit on the left of a number of two or more digits cannot be equal to 0. Since the digits in the thousands column are all different, their sum must be at least $1 + 2 + 3 + 4 = 10$. But since the result has only four digits, one of the following is wrong: A, B, C, or D. But their sum must be at least $1 + 1 + 2 + 3 = 7$.

Now, according to the units column, x must be an even number. Therefore, $x = 8$. In the same column one can deduce that D is 1 or 6. But there must be a carryover of 2 to the second column in order to maintain its parity. Therefore, D is 6 and C is 4. Therefore, D is incorrect in the thousands column, since C is 4 and A and B are 1 or 2 or 2 and 1 and D is 1. The hundreds column cannot contribute a carryover but receives a carryover of 1. Therefore, E must be 3, and B must be 1.

The error arose in writing a D instead of a B in the thousands column.

(See E. R. Emmet, *A Diversity of Puzzles* [Totowa, N.J.: Barnes & Noble, 1977].)

85. *Practical Trisection*

Here is the articulated device invented by Laisant in 1885 (?) for trisecting angles. The circled parts represent joints, and the parts within squares are sliding points. Two deformable rhombuses have a common angle that guarantees that the three angles originating at the apex will all be equal.

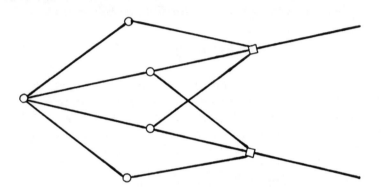

86. The Bandbox

There are eleven different ways of assembling three bandboxes illustrated below. But they are not limited to these few unless one assumes implicitly that the constructions may not place smaller lengths beside the square of the base. If this prohibition is waived, then there are an infinite number of constructions.

In only one of these constructions does a part of a bandbox protrude over its base.

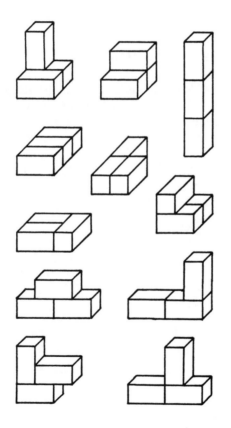

87. A Multicolored Chessboard

It will require at least four colors: on a board 2×2 any two squares can be linked by one move of the king.

Four colors are enough, for if one juxtaposes the 2×2 squares, each one filled in the same manner with four colors, one arrives at the solution:

A B A B . . .
C D C D
A B A B
C D C D

88. Breaking the Chain

To open one link is clearly insufficient. That leaves 3 segments of chain of lengths 1, a, and b. Recombining those will produce a maximum of seven different lengths: 1, a, b, $a + 1$, $b + 1$, $a + b$, and $a + b + 1$, which cannot cover the twenty-three lengths. Opening 2 links, which leaves 5 segments of chain, permits many more combinations. In fact, one can solve the problem by the following division: 3—1—6—1—12.

Opening two links suffices.

89. *What's It Good For?*

Let p be a point on the vertical tangent to the circle and t the point of contact of another tangent from p. If the angle apt is given, it is possible to make the apparatus coincide so that pt is tangent to the circle. In that case b and c determine the two trisectors of the angle, since the angles pab, pbc, and pct are equal.

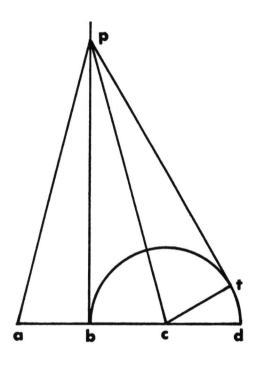

90. Reversible Magic

If the five rows of the square have the same sum, the sum of the twenty-five palindromes has to be divisible by five. Let us see whether that sum ends in a 5 or a 0. The twenty-five numerical palindromes beginning with 11 are 11, 22 . . . , 99, 101, 111, 121 . . . , 191, 202 . . . , 252. Since the sum of their units in the digits place is 67, the sum of the twenty-five numbers cannot be divisible by 5. Therefore, no magic square can be made with them.

91. A Cross and a Square

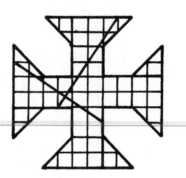

92. The Finishing Touch

The second player has an assured win. He is certain to fill in the last square if he leaves his opponent either two empty squares that are not aligned or two different alignments of two empty squares.

The second player can always reintroduce that position regardless of his opponent's tactics. If the offensive is on two or three squares, he completes a T, an L, or a cross of five squares. If the offensive is on one square, he makes a right angle of three squares. Regardless of the other's countermoves, he maintains the winning position.

(See Silverman, *Your Move* [New York: McGraw-Hill, 1974].)

93. Back to Trisection

Here is the apparatus that will trisect any angle. All the fixed arms are of equal length. The square indicates a sliding joint, and the rhombuses provide the fundamental property of the structure.

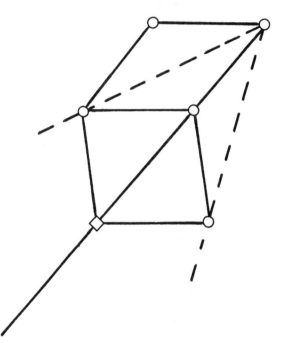

94. *The Symmetrical Cross*

This solution requires seven scissor cuts, but it produces a perfectly symmetrical combination of pieces.

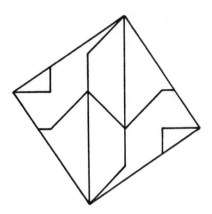

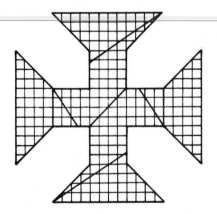

95. Century Sundays

In determining what centuries start on Sunday, the first pitfall to avoid is, of course, to start a century on a year that is a multiple of 100. In other words, the next century begins on January 1, 2001.

What one must do is to make certain calculations, modulo 7; that is, to consider only remainders to that modulus. Every normal year containing 365 days shifts the day by one notch, and leap years by two. Thus, in calculating from January 1, 1978, to January 1, 2001, there are 23 years of which 6 are leap years, which leaves a remainder of 1 and places January 1, 2001, on a Monday.

Only years divisible by 400 have the extra leap-year day. Therefore, it follows, that a century requires an adjustment of 2 for the 100 years plus 3 for the 24 leap years, giving a total of 5. The result is the following first days for the centuries: 2001: Monday; 2101: Saturday; 2201: Thursday; 2301: Tuesday; 2401: Monday.

The adjustment at the end of 4 centuries being 0, these are the only days that come up; none of these centuries starts on a Sunday.

96. To Have or Not to Have

The distributions have the same probability, since it is obvious that if you and your partner do not hold any of the cards in question, your opponents will hold them all.

97. *The Area of the Slice*

In this problem, *abc* is equilateral, and its area if $\pi/6$. To it must be added the areas x and y, which belong to the rectangle *dfge*, along with the rest of the section, or $1 - \dfrac{\sqrt{3}}{2}$. The total of these areas is $\pi/6 + 1 - \dfrac{\sqrt{3}}{2}$, which comes to approximately 0.658.

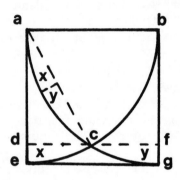

98. *Integral Triangles*

Let us designate the three sides x, y, z and apply Heiron's formula for the area:

$$x + y + z = \frac{1}{4} \sqrt{(x + y + z)(x + y - z)(x - y + z)(- x + y + z)}$$

And then:

$$16(x + y + z) = (x + y - z)(x - y + z)(- x + y + z)$$

Now those factors are either all odd or all even, since they differ from one another by twice two of the sides. They are all even, therefore, since their product is an even number. One can therefore conclude:

$$x + y - z = 2k$$
$$y = \frac{(k^2 + 4)(x - k)}{kx - (k^2 + 4)}$$
$$z = x + y - 2k$$

One obtains for $k = 1$ and $k = 2$:

$$5, 12, 13$$
$$6, \ 8, 10$$
$$6, 25, 29$$
$$7, 15, 20$$
$$9, 10, 17$$

The other values repeat these solutions.

(See Stephen Ainley, *Mathematical Puzzles*, 1977.)

99. Vases

This is a standard problem when the capacity of the third vase is given. But I have seen it solved in the following way, without knowing in advance the capacity of the third vase. Two equations can be set up. Let $5x - 3y = 4$, with the solution that $x = 2$ and $y = 2$, which suggests 3 pints in the first vase, 5 in the second, and none in the third. We start with this combination (3, 5, 0) and then 3, 0, 5; 0, 3, 5; 3, 3, 2; 1, 5, 2; 1, 0, 7; 0, 1, 7; 3, 1, 4.

Let $3x - 5y = 4$, which gives the solution $x = 3$ and $y = 1$, suggesting 3, 5, 0; 0, 5, 3; 3, 2, 3; 0, 2, 6; 2, 0, 6; 2, 5, 1; 3, 4, 1; 0, 4, 4. With the last method, 6 pints suffice for the third vase.

100. Writer's Cramp

Since he produces 1/50 page a day when he has only 1 page left to write, daily writing speed is 1/50 the balance as a general rule. As he starts with a speed of 1/10, that means that the work contains 5 pages. The first page took him 10 days; the second page, at 4/50 a day, 12½ days; the third page, at 3/50 a day, 16⅔ days; the fourth day, at 2/50 a day, 25 days; the fifth page, 50 days, making 114⅙ days all told.

101. Lining Up Blacks and Whites

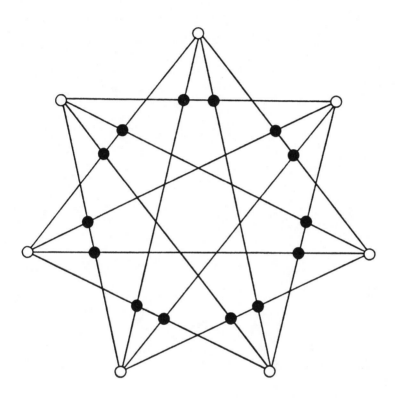

102. More Alignments

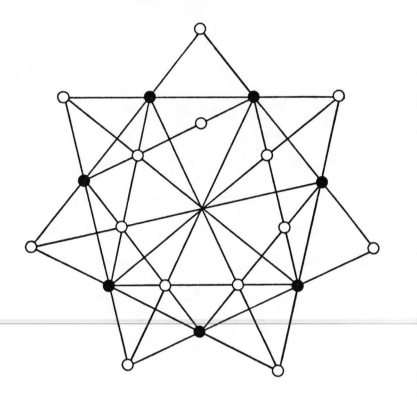

103. Trisection in the Enlightenment

For trisecting angles, the apparatus is made up only of two external arms with rods of equal lengths:

$$CD = BD = DF = DE = AB = AC$$

The little circles indicate fixed joints, and the little rectangles indicate sliding ones. The angle EDF is three times the angle BAC. For the angle DBE is the exterior angle of the isosceles triangle DAB, and accordingly equal to BAC, and also to DEB since BDE is isosceles. The angle GDE is exterior to ADE and therefore equal to one and one-half times the angle BAC. Its double FDE is three times BAC. To make a division by five (quintisection?), one must attach additional arms and of equal length: GF, GE, GH, and GI. The angle HGI is the quintuple of angle ABC. It is apparent that the device described in problem 89 can be adapted to dividing an angle by five, with the advantage of also dividing it by four; but with the disadvantage of having to add five supplementary rods instead of four.

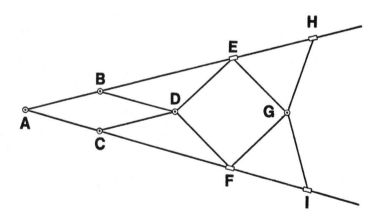

105. Pi in an Unfamiliar Context

The first decoupage gives a regular hexagon, of which the sides are the six linear parts. The second decoupage gives a rectangle.

106. Toward Unity

The sum of the two numbers will obviously be 1 without any need to invoke the concept of limits if one can find two fractions $\frac{a}{b}$ and $\frac{b-a}{b}$ such that the two numbers are those of the decimal expressions.

The first fraction must be a little less than 2/10. What is the denominator? $\frac{1}{6} = 0.17$ . . . is too large; $\frac{1}{7} = 0.14$ . . . is too small. Let us try 2/11, 2/12, 2/13. . . . This last fraction works, and so the two fractions are the decimal expressions of 2/13 and 11/13, respectively.

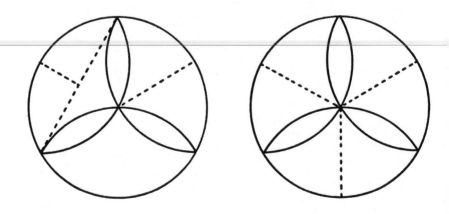

104. The Odds on the White Card

Be careful about calculating the probabilities in this experiment. There are not two equally probable events, but actually three.

In fact, the white side showing can be either one side of the white card, the other side of the white card, or the white side of the red-and-white card. Thus, there are two chances in three, and not one in two, that the other side is white. So I should give you two to one odds on the white card or six dollars against three. If I offer you less than that, the odds are on my side.

107. An Accidental Ellipse

An ellipse is described by each point (except the top) of a pair of folding household steps, in the shape of an old-fashioned stile. This happens when the hinge at the top breaks and the two sets of steps tumble to the ground, one of the feet of one set being propped against a wall. The diagram below shows the cross-section of the steps in boldface lines, the one half blocked by the wall at point 0. If the two steps are of length a, the prolongation of the second as far as the wall is the same length. An arbitrary point is the distance r from the top and has as its coordinates x and y. The lengths x' and y' complement them on the sides of the large right-angle triangle. The similarity of the two triangles gives us $\dfrac{y}{y}$ and $\dfrac{a - 2}{a + r}$. By the Pythagorean theorem, $x^2 + y'^2 = (a + r)^2$. From this one can deduce that

$$\frac{x^2}{(a + 2)^2} + \frac{y^2}{(a - r)^2} = 1.$$

Thus, the point must describe a quarter ellipse with axes $a - r$ and $a + r$.

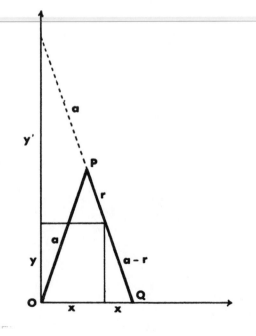

108. Your Basic Boat

Although it would appear to violate the laws of physics, such a boat is possible and has been entered in special races in England. The "motor" consists of a rope attached to the stern. To move the boat forward, the crew gives the rope a series of short, sharp jerks. The system depends on a certain friction effect of the water and would not work in the absence of such a medium (say, in outer space).

It is thus possible to displace the center of gravity of such a craft by a process involving three steps:

1) A displacement of the center of gravity toward the stern; as one leans forward this creates a slight forward motion of the boat checked by the resistance of the water.
2) A displacement toward the bow similarly retarded by friction.
3) The sudden tension of the rope, which transmits kinetic energy to the boat, providing an obviously more powerful impulse than the effect of the two preceding steps.

It is possible to achieve a speed of 3 knots by this means.

(See Rouse-Ball, *Mathematical Recreations*, rev. ed. [New York: Macmillan, 1960].)

109. Points and Lines

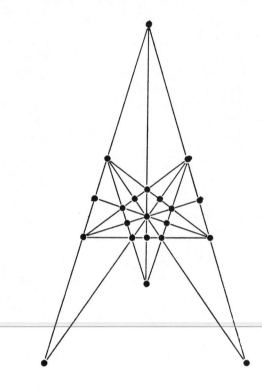

110. Squaring the Square

If you have tried to juxtapose two geometric squares to form a third, you have bumped up against what seems—so far—an impossibility.

On the other hand, it is possible to juxtapose the squares of two numbers. For example, 4 and 9, the squares of 2 and 3, can be put together to make 49, the square of 7. The exploration of such numbers appears to require trial and error. Here are others up to 100,000: 169, 361, 1225, 1444, 1681, 3249, 4225, 15625, 16900, 36100, 42025, 49729, 64009, 81225, 93025.

(Problem 134 is a further extension of this problem.)

111. The Missing Token

The sum total of the tokens being $1 + 2 + 3 + 4 + 5 + 6 + 7 + 8 + 9 = 45$, the sum of the remaining tokens is not divisible by 3 unless the missing one is also so divisible. Thus, it has to be 0, 3, 6, or 9, which reveals that the sum of the remaining tokens is 45, 42, 39, or 36. Only one of these totals is divisible by 4, which proves that it must have been the 9 token that was lost. But these conditions are not sufficient. One must first prove that the groups can, in fact, be formed. There are (8,3,1), (0,7,5), (6,4,2), and (8,1), (7,2), (6,3), and (5,4,0).

112. Quadrature and Dissection

Two cuts suffice to turn two juxtaposed squares into a third. (The arrows indicate two equal lengths.)

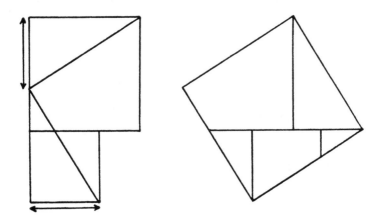

113. An Uneasy Cryptogram

In his bathtub Jack saw an indigo cockroach trying to climb out. It had a jaunty air and a wisp of grass in its mouth. This was Jack's first warning of drug addiction.

This message has the unusual feature of containing no E's, in spite of the frequency of that letter in English spelling. The cipher itself involves a method of alphabetical substitution ascribed to Julius Caesar.

For each letter of the plaintext the letter 15 places subsequent in the alphabet has been substituted. Because the text uses no Es, that letter has been omitted altogether, leaving a 25-letter alphabet.

114. Roots

Assume that you wish to find the square root of n for which a is a rough approximation greater than $\dfrac{\sqrt{n}}{2}$. This approximation a can be improved systematically by the formula $m = \dfrac{a^2 - n}{2a}$.

If m is positive, a is too large by that amount, if m is negative, a must be increased accordingly. The corrected value of a is used to calculate a second value for m and so on iteratively until one arrives at the desired result $a^2 - n = 0$. The advantage of performing these steps on a pocket calculator is obvious. If it has a memory function, this can be performed without pencil and paper.

115. The Triangulation of the Triangle

The lines joining the midpoints of the sides yield an immediate solution, if we remember that they are parallel to the respective corresponding sides.

From this we can draw a general principle: if two triangles have two isometric sides and angles corresponding to these supplementary sides, then there is a way of cutting that transforms one into the other.

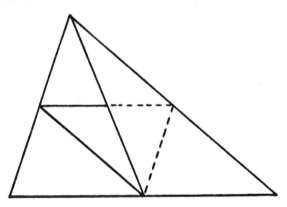

116. Travels on the Hexagon

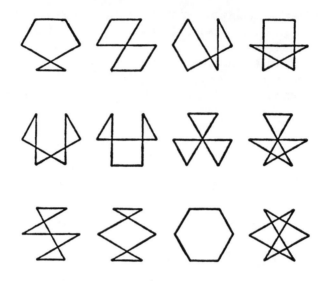

117. A Bailout Fee

One can assume that the workman's charge is based on the price for raising his pulley one unit of length. Let us call x the price after emptying the first pailful, which he has raised a mean height of ½ yard. The second pailful raised a mean height of 1½ yards costs three times as much. The third costs five times as much, and so on. Thus the first 10 yards cost $100x = x(1 + 3 + \ldots + 19)$ while 20 yards cost $x(1 + 3 + \ldots + 39) = 400x$. Accordingly, the workman is owed $100. Calculus buffs can verify that this example comes out. If the worker had used a pump and worked continuously, the result would be the same.

118. A Prize Hamster

Naturally, there is a logical pattern governing the succession. Each price was arrived at by adding to the previous price the sum of the square of its digits:

$$425 + 16 + 4 + 25 = 470, \text{ etc.}$$
$$802 + 64 + 0 + 4 = 870.$$

119. The Women Man the Oars

There are eight crossings of the boat; the letters designate the men and the numbers the wives:

A1B2C3D4

A1BCD	234
A1B2CD	34
ABCD	1234
A1BCD	234
A1	B2C3D4
A1B2	C3D4
A1	B2C3D4
	A1B2C3D4

120. Breaking Up a Year

As the first operation shows, it is not helpful to deal in 1s. It's not any more helpful to introduce three 2s as factors, since $3 \times 3 > 2 \times 2 \times 2$. 4s are not helpful as $4 = 2 + 2 = 2 \times 2$. One should avoid the digits 5 and larger: $3 \times 2 > 5, 3 \times 3 > 6$, and more generally, $(n - 2) \times 2 > n$. There remain 3s and a pair of 2s since $1980 = 660 \times 3$. The number in question is 3^{660}.

121. Protagoras at the Bar

If the court decides that Protagoras is in the right and wins his case, the problem is resolved. But actually the court can only make its decisions relative to events that have already taken place. It cannot deliver a judgment bearing on an event that is in the process of taking place. Consequently, since up to the most recent past the student has not won a case, the court must sustain his right not to pay.

But afterward, at the very moment the trial is over, the status of the student has changed: he has, in fact, won a case. Protagoras can now, through a second suit, make a valid claim for payment of his fee. He will win that one with certainty and get paid—if the student has the money. But the situation called for two lawsuits instead of one.

122. *Squaring Polygons*

Here is one solution for transforming the irregular but symmetrical decagon into a square by cutting it into eight pieces. Note that it has been necessary to turn over one of the pieces. Some puzzle fans have done even better, coming up with different ways of creating a square out of seven pieces. At least one person believes it is possible to do even better than that!

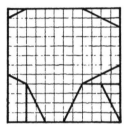
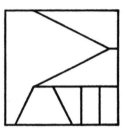

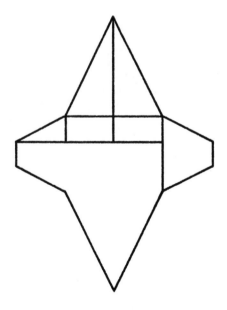

123. Drawing the Line

The solution is presented in two steps, the start and the finish.
They would be illegible if one tried to combine them.

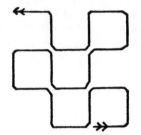

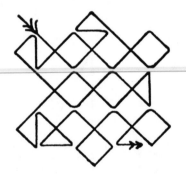

124. A Band of Five Squares Creates Another Square

It is obviously necessary to introduce $\sqrt{5}$ in order to guide the process of trial and error.

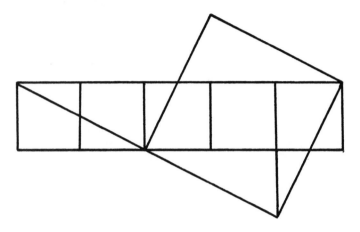

125. The Fifth Power

This can be proved by induction by showing that if it is true for $n = k$, it will be true for $n = k + 1$.

A simpler "empirical" approach is to note that all numbers end in 0, 1, . . . or 9, and the fifth power of 0, 1, . . . 9 end, respectively, in 0, 1, . . . 9, as you can verify by a table or laborious calculation. Therefore, the last digit of the fifth power of a number is the last digit of the number itself. Thus, $n^5 - n$ ends with a 0 and is divisible by 5.

126. A Line to Follow

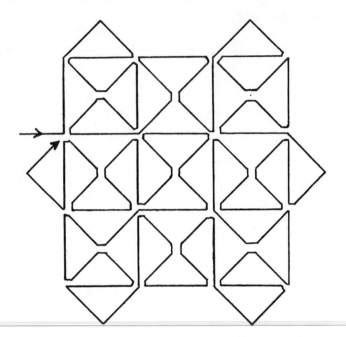

127. A Tricky Division

Here is a way to cut up the rest of a square into four congruent parts after a quarter of it has been removed in the form of a triangle. One has to be bold enough to imagine the unfamiliar shapes A*a*, B*b*, C*c*, and D*d*.
(See *Royal Magazine*, November 1930)

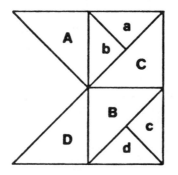

128. Unlisted Numbers

In order to eliminate the six-digit numbers containing 12, we shall distinguish five classes of numbers according to these forms:

A	1	2	.	.	.	.
B	.	1	2	.	.	.
C	.	.	1	2	.	.
D	.	.	.	1	2	.
E	.	.	.	.	1	2

Each class contains 10^4 numbers. There is no number common to AB, BC, CD, DE. On the other hand, AC, AD, AE, BD, BE, CE each have 10^2 numbers in common. Additionally, there is a number common to AEC: 121212.

Therefore, the number of numbers to be excluded is $5 \times 10^4 + 1 - 6 \times 10^2 = 49{,}401$.

129. No Way to Make a Square

Except for the number 1 itself, no number composed of 1s exclusively can be the square of an integer.

This is made clear by an examination of the composition of such numbers, each of which can be expressed in the form $11 + 100n = 4(25n + 2) + 3$.

It is obvious that such numbers, if divided by 4, will always leave a remainder 3.

As for the squares of integers, they are either even numbers of the form $4p^2$ or odd numbers of the form $(2n + 1)^2 = 4n^2 + 4n + 1$. Therefore, the remainder of any square of a whole number upon division by 4 is either 0 or 1. For that reason, no number made up of 1 (other than 1) can be the square of an integer.

130. A Primary Law

$p^2 - 1 = (p + 1)(p - 1)$

Since p is a prime and therefore an odd number, and therefore not divisible by 3, one of the two numbers $(p - 1)$ and $(p + 1)$ is divisible by 2 and the other by 4.

Also, one of the two numbers $(p - 1)$ and $(p + 1)$ is divisible by 3. Therefore $p^2 - 1 = (p + 1)(p - 1) = 2 \times 3 \times 4m = 24m$.

This proof makes it abundantly clear that p need not be a prime but need only be odd and not divisible by 3 (e.g., 25, 35, 49, etc.). Thus, the underlying equation is satisfied by one out of every three integers.

131. Ten Digits for One

Here are six fractions expressing 9 in which all ten digits appear once and only once:

$$9 = \frac{57429}{06381} = \frac{58239}{06471} = \frac{75249}{08361}$$

$$= \frac{95742}{10638} = \frac{95823}{10647} = \frac{97524}{10836}$$

The search for this is helped by observing that the last digits of the denominator and the numerator must be divisible by 9. It is also helpful to try to start with an approximative division by 9—approximately 54, giving 6, etc. Of course, sticklers will object to the appearance of the 0s in the first three expressions. There seems to be no other way of tackling this problem.
(See *Moscow Puzzles: Three Hundred Fifty-Nine Mathematical Recreations*, [New York: Charles Scribner's Sons, 1972].)

132. Inside Out

An individual triangle remains on the inside or the outside. In order to prove that, it is sufficient to trace a line starting on the outside of the figure and ending up on the inside of the triangle. Each time that that line follows the necessary course, it will pass alternatively from the outside to the inside and from the inside to the outside. Therefore, the position of the triangle depends on the parity (odd or even) of the number of traversals. But that number remains the same for each triangle regardless of the nature of the solution.

133. Raindrops Are Falling . . .

Let us suppose that a man is h feet high, e feet thick, and r feet wide and that he traverses a distance l in a time t. We shall also assume that the amount of water in the air (i.e., the number of raindrops) is proportional to the volume m^3. We also assume that the rain is falling perpendicularly to the ground with the velocity v (there being virtually no wind). During the time t in which he runs the distance l, he will receive the amount of rain contained in two parallelepipeds: (1) the horizontal surface he exposes to the rain striking him from above multiplied by the height of the column of rain that will fall in time t (this is the same as the amount of rain that would fall on him if he stood still for t seconds), that is, $r \times e \times v \times t$; (2) the second parallelepiped is the vertical surface he exposes to the rain as he runs through it, that is, $r \times h \times l$. Combining the volumes of the two parallelepipeds, one obtains volume $r(lh + evt)$, and the amount of rain that strikes him = $Q = dr(lh + evt)$. It is immediately apparent that the function Q increases with increasing t. To stay as dry as possible, he must run as fast as possible. Of course, perfectionists can carry this calculation further by considering the advantage of leaning over, what to do if there's a wind, etc.

134. Remarkable Quadratures

This wonderful number is $4,950,625 = 2225^2$. It can be decomposed as $4 = 2^2$ and $950,625 = 975^2$ or $49 = 7^2$ and $50,625 = 225^2$.

135. *Möbius and His Better Half*

This is how to cut the Möbius strip in a straight line without touching more than one edge. The figure represents the strip before it is given the half turn and fastened at the ends. Thus the problem is reduced to cutting in the straight line *a b c d e*. One can verify that the areas are equal by adding up the components.

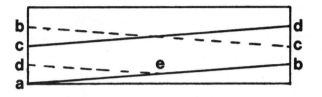

136. *Quadruple Quadrature*

One solution is $19,025^2 = 361,950,625$, where $361 = 19^2$ and $950,625 = 975^2$ and where $36 = 6^2$, $1 = 1^2$, $9 = 3^2$, and $50,625 = 225^2$. Another solution is $90,125^2 = 8,122,515,625$, where one recognizes 81,225, 1 and 5,625 as squares, as well as $81,225 = 285^2$ and $15,625 = 125^2$. The reader might like to explore the possibility of a systematic production of these quadruple quadratics rather than discovering them through trial and error.

137. Something New About Nines

We must prove that every integral square of two digits or more contains at least one even digit.

All the two-digit squares have that property: 16, 25, 36, and 81. Every other square is 100 or greater. Now, the square of a number greater than 10 is greater than 100 and can be expressed in the form $(10d + u)^2 = 100d^2 + 20du + u^2$, where u is not less than 1. Since the units digit is the same as the units digit of u^2, the property is established for u = 0, 2, 4, 6, 8. If $u = 1$, in $100d^2 + 20d + 1$, the digit in the tens column is given by $2d$, which is even. The reader can verify for himself that for $u = 3, 5, 7, 9$ there will be an even number in the tens column.

138. The Trisection of Pappus

To prove that the construction attributed to Pappus is in fact one-third of the given angle, let us first produce a circle with its center at *e*, the midpoint of *cd*, and passing through *a*. Since *aeo* is isosceles, the angles numbered 2 are equal. One of them is the exterior angle of *ead* and therefore equal to the sum of the two angles numbered 1.

(See Asger Aaboe, *Episodes from the Early History of Mathematics* [New Mathematical Library, No. 13, 1975].)

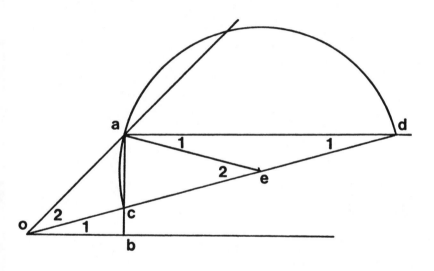

139. Archimedes Cuts It Up

Here is the square as cut up by Archimedes in order to obtain fourteen pieces, each in a rational relation to the whole, the fractions expressing forty-eighths. The computation of each is elementary.

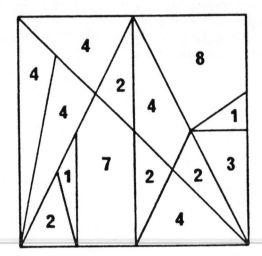

140. Tails I Win

The simplest way to approach this problem is to note that at the very start of the game there is a probability of ½ that tails will come up and the first player will win. For the second player to win on *his* first toss, the probability is ½ × ½ = ¼ (the probability of heads on the first player's toss times the probability of tails on the second player's toss). Since the first player's chances will always remain twice the second player's in every pair of tosses and since the sum of their probabilities has to be 1, since one has to win, the probability of winning is ⅔ and ⅓ for the first and second players, respectively.

141. The Barrier of Thirst

Should the author of this solution be proud of it? Leave with four and a half days' supply of water and a companion who carries a five-day supply. At the end of a day and a half, your companion decides not to go on living. You now have a six-and-a-half-day supply of water. Leaving a one-and-a-half-day supply where you are, you complete the trip to your goal and return to your starting point, picking up the extra supply on the way back. Can one do better? Yes, indeed. Take a look at problem 150.

142. Regrouping the Pieces

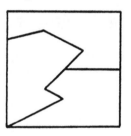

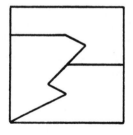

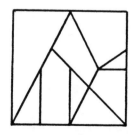

143. A Square for a Compass

Draw a circle and retain the opening of the legs of the compass. Starting with a point A, chosen arbitrarily on the circumference, and without changing the compass, find the three points B, C, and D. Thus, A will be diametrically opposed to D. Using again your center A, trace a circle passing through C and then at D for an arc passing through B and meeting the preceding one at E. OE is the side of the square. In fact,

$$\begin{aligned} OE &= \sqrt{AE^2 - R^2} \\ &= \sqrt{AC^2 - R^2} \\ &= \sqrt{(R\sqrt{3})^2 - R2} \\ &= R\sqrt{2} \end{aligned}$$

144. Words and Numbers

Here is one method inspired by the work of the mathematical logician Kurt Gödel that permits one to associate with each word composed of letters or other symbols a number composed of digits. One begins by assigning to each letter the number representing its position in the alphabet from 1 to 26. Each word is then represented by a product in which the first prime numbers in succession are raised to the powers of the successive numbers (i.e., places in the alphabet) of the letters spelling the word. Thus, $ART = 2^1 \, 3^{18} \, 5^{20}$. The conversion of this number back to the original word is accomplished by decomposing the product into its prime factors and assigning to the power of each prime factor the corresponding letter of the word.

145. *Words, Numbers, and Sentences*

To be able to associate a number with a sentence in an unambiguous way, one can use again the method described in problem 144, but one must take certain precautions in order to avoid ambiguity. One must now assign to each letter an *odd* number: 3 for A, 5 for B, etc., 53 for Z.

Let us assign to each word the product of the first prime numbers raised to the powers corresponding to the numbers of the individual letters. Thus, ARTS = $2^3 3^{37} 5^{41} 7^{39}$ and FINE = $2^{13} 3^{19} 5^{29} 7^{11}$. We can now assign to an entire sentence the *product* of the first successive prime numbers raised to the numbers of its words. Thus, FINE ARTS = $2^{FINE} 3^{ARTS}$. Ambiguity is eliminated since the power of 2 is odd for a word and even for a sentence.

146. *A Triangle in a Square*

There are two possible ways of inscribing a triangle in a square:
1) Let the point of origin of one angle be at an apex of the square with the two other angles touching the sides that do not meet at the apex.
2) Let each of its three angles touch a side.

The first possibility leads to an equilateral triangle with a side that is greater than the side of the square.

The second possibility leads to an equilateral triangle of which one side can at its minimum be equal to a side of the square if there is parallelism. This is then the answer one is seeking. One apex touches the middle of a side of the square, and the opposite side of the triangle is parallel to the opposite side of the square. The triangle and the square have equal sides.

147. Mysterious Powers

Have you defined the properties of this mysterious square? When a number terminates in 12890625, all its integral powers end in the same sequence:

$$\text{if } n = 12890625 = 5^8 \times 33$$
$$n - 1 = 12890624 = 2^8 \times 5083$$
$$n(n - 1) = 10^8 \times q$$
$$n^2 = n + 10^8 \times q$$

Thus, the numbers n and n^2 end in the same digits.

148. Superior Antimagic

One puzzle fan produces numerous magic squares of order 6. Each original solution gave him twenty-three varieties having at least twenty digits out of place. "It suffices to permute the lines and columns in the same order. If the original is numbered 1, 2, 3, 4, 5, 6, one considers three couples 16, 25, 34, each remaining symmetrically distributed with respect to the medians of the square. One permutes successively one couple, then two, then three." In that way you can achieve your own variation of the square.

5	35	13	34	12	7
6	8	30	23	11	27
32	28	17	16	20	2
33	9	22	21	18	15
10	26	4	14	29	25
31	1	24	3	19	36

149. Coupled Couples

Here is how they can all get across the river in seven crossings:
   1) Five wives cross.
   2) One wife returns.
   3) Her husband stays with her, and four other men cross.
   4) One couple returns.
   5) Two couples cross.
   6) One couple returns.
   7) The last two couples cross.

150. No Holds Barred

Consider the simple possibility that the planting of the flag after a four-day journey across the desert is the ultimate purpose of your life. In that case you need only bring four days' worth of water and, your goal once achieved, depart from this world. This might be called the kamikaze solution!